CLASSICS *for* YOUNG READERS

Volume 4A

TABLE OF CONTENTS

LESSONS LEARNED

TRICKSTER TALES

STORIES FROM THE BIBLE

LIFE STORIES

POETRY

A PATCHWORK OF PEOPLE

STORIES IN VERSE

LESSONS LEARNED

CHILD'S PLAY
by Laura E. Richards

Once a child was playing on a log that lay by the roadside. Another child came along and stopped to speak to him.

"What are you doing?" asked the second child.

"I am sailing to the Southern Seas," replied the first, "to get a cargo of monkeys, coconuts, and crystal balls as large as oranges. Come up here, and you may sail with me if you like."

So the second child climbed up on the log.

"Look!" said the first child. "See how the foam bubbles up before the ship, and trails and floats away behind! Look! The water is so clear that we can see the fishes swimming about, blue and red and green. There goes a parrot-fish. My father told me about them. I wouldn't be surprised if we saw a whale in a minute."

"What are you talking about?" asked the second child peevishly. "There is no water here, only grass. And anyway, this is nothing but a log. You can't find islands in this way."

"But we have found them," cried the first child. "Here they are now. I see palm-trees waving, and the white sand glittering. Look! There are people gathering to welcome us on the beach. They have feather cloaks, and necklaces, and anklets of copper and gold. Oh! There is an elephant coming straight toward us."

"I should think you would be ashamed," said the second child. "That is the Widow Slocum."

"It's all the same," said the first child.

The second child climbed off the log. "I'm going to play stickball," he said. "I don't see any sense in this. I think you are pretty dull to play things that aren't really there." And he walked away.

The first child looked after him a moment.

"I think you are pretty dull," he said to himself, "to see nothing but what is under your nose."

But he was too well-mannered to say this aloud. And, taking his cargo, he sailed for another port.

CHANTICLEER AND THE FOX

from Geoffrey Chaucer's Canterbury Tales

Once upon a time, in a barnyard close to a wood in a little valley, there lived a rooster named Chanticleer. His bill was shiny black, his comb was redder than coral, and his feathers were like burnished gold. And his voice! Oh, it was wonderful to hear. It was merrier than a sprightly tune played on the church organ. Just before dawn each morning, his crowing sounded over the valley, as regular as a well-wound clock.

This fine rooster had seven fine hens. One night, as he sat on the perch by the side of the fairest of the hens, Dame Partlet, he began to make a curious noise in his throat, like a man having a bad dream.

"What is it, my dear?" said Dame Partlet. "Why do you groan so?"

"Oh!" said Chanticleer, "I had the most horrible dream. I thought that as I roamed down by the wood a beast like a dog sprang out and seized me. His color was red, his nose was small, and his eyes were like coals of fire. Ugh! It was terrible!"

"Tut, tut!" Dame Partlet clucked, "are you a coward to be frightened by a dream? You've been eating more than was good for you. I wish my husband to be wise and brave if he would keep my love!" With that she smoothed her feathers and slowly closed her scarlet eyes.

"Oh course you are right, my love," replied Chanticleer. "And yet I have heard of many dreams that warn of danger to come. But we will not talk of it now. I am quite happy to be here by the side of the fairest hen in all the land!"

Dame Partlet half opened one eye and made a pleased sound deep in her throat.

The next morning, Chanticleer flew down from the perch and called his hens about him for their breakfast. He walked about boldly, calling "Cluck! cluck!" at each grain of corn he found. He felt very proud as they all looked at him admiringly. He strutted about in the sunlight, flapping his wings to show off his feathers, and now and then throwing back his head and crowing. His dream was forgotten; there was no fear in his heart.

Now all this time, Reynard, the fox, was lying hidden in the bushes on the edge of the wood bordering the barnyard. Chanticleer walked nearer and nearer the fox's hiding place. Suddenly he saw a butterfly in the grass, and as he stooped toward it, he spied the fox.

"Cok! cok!" he cried in terror, and turned to flee.

But Reynard piped up in his gentlest voice, "Dear friend, why do you go? I only crept down there to hear you sing. Your voice is like an angel's."

Chanticleer paused, turned, and listened.

Reynard spoke on, in soothing tones. "Your father once visited my house; I should so love to see you there, too. I wonder if you remember your father's singing? I never thought to hear so wonderful a voice again—until I heard you sing this morning."

"Oh?" said Chanticleer, as he puffed out his chest feathers.

"I can almost see your father now," said the fox. "He would

stand on tiptoe, stretching out his long slender neck, sending out his glorious voice. He always flapped his wings and closed his eyes before he sang. Do you do it in the same way? Won't you sing just once and let me hear you? I am so anxious to know if you really sing better than your father."

Chanticleer was so pleased with this flattery that he flapped his wings, stood up on tiptoe, shut his eyes, and crowed as loudly as he could.

No sooner had he begun than Reynard sprang forward, caught him by the throat, threw him over his shoulder, and made off toward his den in the woods.

The hens made a loud outcry when they saw Chanticleer being carried off, so that the people in the cottage nearby heard and ran out after the fox. The dog heard and ran yelping after him. The cow ran, the calf ran, and the pigs began to squeal and run, too. The ducks and geese quacked in terror and flew up into the treetops. Never was there such an uproar. Reynard began to feel a bit frightened himself.

Clamped between the fox's teeth, Chanticleer yet managed to say, "How swiftly you do run! If I were you, I should have some fun with those slowpokes who are trying to catch you. Call out to them and say, 'Why do you creep along like snails? Look! I am far ahead of you and shall soon be feasting on this fowl in spite of all of you!'"

Reynard was pleased with this idea. He stopped short, turned to face his pursuers, and opened his mouth. But as soon as he did so, the rooster flew away and perched up in a tree, safely out of reach.

The fox saw he had lost his prey and began his old tricks again. "My dear friend! I'm sure there has been some misunderstanding. I was only proving to you how important you are in the barnyard. See what a commotion we caused! I did not mean to frighten you. Come down now and we will go along together to my home. I have something very interesting to show you there."

"No" said Chanticleer. "You will not catch me again. I have learned to keep my eyes open and my mouth closed. He who does otherwise deserves what he gets."

By this time, Chanticleer's friends were drawing near, so Reynard turned to flee. "And I have learned," he grumbled as he sped away through the wood, "that he who talks when he should be silent deserves to lose what he has gained."

The Bear Boy
a Pueblo tale retold by Joseph Bruchac

Long ago, in a Pueblo village, a boy named Kuo-Haya lived with his father. But his father did not treat him well. In his heart he still mourned the death of his wife, Kuo-Haya's mother, and did not enjoy doing things with his son. He did not teach his boy how to run. He did not show him how to wrestle. He was always too busy.

As a result, Kuo-Haya was a timid boy and walked about stooped over all of the time. When the other boys raced or wrestled, Kuo-Haya slipped away. He spent much of his time alone.

Time passed, and the boy reached the age when his father should have been helping him get ready for his initiation into manhood. Still Kuo-Haya's father paid no attention at all to his son.

One day Kuo-Haya was out walking far from the village, toward the cliffs where the bears lived. Now the people of the village always knew they must stay away from these cliffs, for the bear was a very powerful animal. It was said that if someone saw a bear's tracks and followed them, he might never come back.

But Kuo-Haya had never been told about this. When he came upon the tracks of a bear, Kuo-Haya followed them along an arroyo, a small canyon cut by a winding stream, up into the mesas. The tracks led into a little box canyon below some caves. There, he came upon some bear cubs.

When they saw Kuo-Haya, the little bears ran away. But Kuo-Haya sat down and called to them in a friendly voice.

"I will not hurt you," he said to the bear cubs. "Come and play with me."

The bears walked back out of the bushes. Soon the boy and the bears were playing together. As they played, however, a shadow came over them. Kuo-Haya looked up and saw the mother bear standing above him.

"Where is Kuo-Haya?" the people asked his father.

"I do not know," the father said.

"Then you must find him!"

So the father and the other people of the pueblo began to search for the missing boy. They went through the canyons calling his name. But they found no sign of the boy there. Finally, when they reached the cliffs, the best trackers found his footsteps and the path of the bears. They followed the tracks along the arroyo and up into the mesas to the box canyon. In front of a cave, they saw the boy playing with the bear cubs as the mother bear watched them approvingly, nudging Kuo-Haya now and then to encourage him.

The trackers crept close, hoping to grab the boy and run. But as soon as the mother bear caught their scent, she growled and pushed her cubs and the boy back into the cave.

"The boy is with the bears," the trackers said when they returned to the village.

"What shall we do?" the people asked.

"It is the responsibility of the boy's father," said the medicine man. Then he called Kuo-Haya's father to him.

"You have not done well," said the medicine man. "You are the one who must guide your boy to manhood, but you have neglected him. Now the mother bear is caring for your boy as you should have done all along. She is teaching him to be strong as a young man must be strong. If you love your son, only you can get him back."

Every one of the medicine man's words went into the father's heart like an arrow. He began to realize that he had been blind to his son's needs because of his own sorrow.

"You are right," he said. "I will go and bring back my son."

Kuo-Haya's father went along the arroyo and climbed the cliffs. When he came to the bear's cave, he found Kuo-Haya wrestling with the little bears. As the father watched, he saw that his son seemed more sure of himself than ever before.

"Kuo-Haya," he shouted. "Come to me."

The boy looked at him and then just walked into the cave. Although the father tried to follow, the big mother bear stood up on her hind legs and growled. She would not allow the father to come any closer.

So Kuo-Haya's father went back to his home. He was angry now. He began to gather together his weapons, and brought out his bow and his arrows and his lance. But the medicine man came to his lodge and showed him the bear claw that he wore around his neck.

"Those bears are my relatives!" the medicine man said. "You must not harm them. They are teaching your boy how we should care for each other, so you must not be cruel to them. You must get your son back with love, not violence."

Kuo-Haya's father prayed for guidance. He went outside and sat on the ground. As he sat there, a bee flew up to him, right by his face. Then it flew away. The father stood up. Now he knew what to do!

"Thank you, Little Brother," he said. He began to make his preparations. The medicine man watched what he was doing and smiled.

Kuo-Haya's father went to the place where the bees had their hives. He made a fire and put green branches on it so that it made smoke. Then he blew the smoke into the tree where the bees were. The bees soon went to sleep.

Carefully Kuo-Haya's father took out some honey from their hive. When he was done, he placed pollen and some small pieces of turquoise at the foot of the tree to thank the bees for their gift. The medicine man, who was watching all this, smiled again. Truly the father was beginning to learn.

Kuo-Haya's father traveled again to the cliffs where the bears lived. He hid behind a tree and saw how the mother bear treated Kuo-Haya and the cubs with love. He saw that Kuo-Haya was able to hold his own as he wrestled the bears.

He came out from his hiding place, put the honey on the ground and stepped back. "My friends," he said, "I have brought you something sweet."

The mother bear and her cubs came over and began to eat the honey. While they ate, Kuo-Haya's father went to the boy. He saw that his little boy was now a young man.

"Kuo-Haya," he said, putting his hands on his son's shoulders, "I have come to take you home. The bears have taught me a lesson. I shall treat you as a father should treat his son."

"I will go with you, Father," said the boy. "But I, too, have learned things from the bears. They have shown me how we must care for one another. I will come with you only if you promise you will always be friends with the bears."

The father promised, and that promise was kept. Not only was he friends with the bears, but he showed his boy the love a son deserves. And he taught him all the things a son should be taught.

Everyone in the village soon saw that Kuo-Haya, the bear boy, was no longer the timid little boy he had been. Because of what the bears had taught him, he was the best wrestler among the boys. With his father's help, Kuo-Haya quickly became the greatest runner of all. To this day, his story is told to remind all parents that they must always show as much love for their children as there is in the heart of a bear.

THE KING AND HIS HAWK

retold by James Baldwin

Genghis Khan was a great king and warrior. He led his army into China and Persia, and he conquered many lands. In every country, men told about his daring deeds. They said that since Alexander the Great, there had been no king like him.

One morning when he was home from the wars, he rode out into the woods to have a day's sport. Many of his friends were with him. They rode out gaily, carrying their bows and arrows. Behind them came the servants with the hounds.

It was a merry hunting party. The woods rang with their shouts and laughter. They expected to carry much game home in the evening.

On the king's wrist sat his favorite hawk. For in those days hawks were trained to hunt. At a word from their masters, they would fly high up into the air and look around for prey. If they chanced to see a deer or a rabbit, they would swoop down upon it swift as any arrow.

All day long Genghis Khan and his huntsmen rode through the woods. But they did not find as much game as they expected.

Toward evening they started for home. The king had often ridden through the woods, and he knew all the paths. So while the rest of the party took the nearest way, he went by a longer road through a valley between two mountains.

The day had been warm, and the king was very thirsty. His pet hawk had left his wrist and flown away. It would be sure to find its way home.

The king rode slowly along. He had once seen a spring of clear water near this pathway. If he could only find it now! But the hot days of summer had dried up all the mountain brooks.

At last, to his joy, he saw some water trickling down over the edge of a rock. He knew that there was a spring farther up. In the wet season, a swift stream of water always poured down here. But now it came only one drop at a time.

The king leaped from his horse. He took a little silver cup from his hunting bag. He held it so as to catch the slowly falling drops.

It took a long time to fill the cup. The king was so thirsty that he could hardly wait. At last it was nearly full. He put the cup to his lips, and was about to drink.

All at once there was a whirring sound in the air, and the cup was knocked from his hands. The water was all spilled upon the ground.

The king looked up to see who had done this thing. It was his pet hawk.

The hawk flew back and forth a few times, and then alighted among the rocks by the spring.

The king picked up the cup, and again held it to catch the trickling drops.

This time he did not wait so long. When the cup was half full, he lifted it toward his mouth. But before it had touched his lips, the hawk swooped down again and knocked it from his hands.

And now the king began to grow angry. He tried again, and for the third time the hawk kept him from drinking.

The king was now very angry indeed.

"How do you dare to act so?" he cried. "If I had you in my hands, I would wring your neck!"

Then he filled the cup again. But before he tried to drink, he drew his sword.

"Now, Sir Hawk," he said, "this is the last time."

He had hardly spoken, before the hawk swooped down and knocked the cup from his hand. But the king was looking for this. With a quick sweep of the sword he struck the bird as it passed.

The next moment the poor hawk lay bleeding and dying at its master's feet.

"That is what you get for your pains," said Genghis Khan.

But when he looked for his cup he found that it had fallen between two rocks, where he could not reach it.

"At any rate, I will have a drink from that spring," he said to himself.

He began to climb the steep bank to the place from which the water trickled. It was hard work, and the higher he climbed, the thirstier he became.

At last he reached the place. There indeed was a pool of water. But what was that lying in the pool, and almost filling it? It was a huge, dead snake of the most poisonous kind.

The king stopped. He forgot his thirst. He thought only of the poor dead bird lying on the ground below him.

"The hawk saved my life!" he cried, "and how did I repay him? He was my best friend, and I have killed him."

He clambered down the bank. He took the bird up gently, and laid it in his hunting bag. Then he mounted his horse and rode swiftly home. He said to himself, "I have learned a sad lesson today, and that is, never to do anything in anger."

It Could Always Be Worse

Once there was a poor Jewish man who had come to the end of his rope. So he went to his rabbi, a holy teacher, for advice.

"Holy Rabbi!" he cried. "Things are in a bad way with me, and are getting worse all the time! We are poor, so poor, that my wife, my six children, my in-laws and I have to live in a one-room hut. We get in each other's way all the time. Our nerves are frayed and, because we have plenty of trouble, we quarrel. Believe me—my home is awful, and things could not possibly be worse!"

The rabbi pondered the matter gravely. "My son," he said, "promise to do as I tell you and your condition will improve."

"I promise, Rabbi," answered the troubled man. "I'll do anything you say."

"Tell me—what animals do you own?"

"I have a cow, a goat, and some chickens."

"Very well! Go home now and take all these animals into your house to live with you."

The poor man was amazed, but since he had promised the rabbi, he went home and brought all the animals into his house.

The following day the poor man returned to the rabbi and cried, "Rabbi, what misfortune have you brought upon me! I did as you told me and brought the animals into the house. And now what have I got? Things are worse than ever! The house is turned into a barn! Save me, Rabbi—help me!"

"My son," replied the rabbi calmly, "go home and take the chickens out of your house. God will help you."

So the poor man went home and took the chickens out of his house. But it was not long before he again came running to the rabbi.

"Holy Rabbi!" he wailed. "Help me, save me! The goat is smashing everything in the house. She's turning my life into a nightmare."

"Go home," said the rabbi gently, "and take the goat out of the house. God will help you!"

The poor man returned to his house and removed the goat. But it wasn't long before he again came running to the rabbi, crying loudly, "What a misfortune you've brought upon my head, Rabbi! The cow has turned my house into a stable! How can you expect a human being to live side by side with an animal?"

"You're right—a hundred times right!" agreed the rabbi. "Go straight home and take the cow out of your house!"

And the poor unfortunate man hurried home and took the cow out of his house.

Not a day passed before he came running again to the rabbi. "Rabbi!" cried the poor man, his face beaming. "You've made life sweet again for me. With all the animals out, the house is so quiet, so roomy, and so clean! What a pleasure!"

THE GREEN GLASS BALL

an Irish folktale
dramatized by Hazel W. Corson

Characters

TINKER
DONKEY
TERRY
TWO WOMEN
BOY
GIRL

TWO MEN
MIKE
BOY'S MOTHER
OLD WOMAN
TIM

SCENE 1

Time: **LONG AGO**

Setting: **A SMALL VILLAGE IN IRELAND**

At Rise: TINKER *and* DONKEY *enter right and walk slowly to center.*

TINKER: 'Tis a beautiful day. The sun is shining! The birds are singing!

DONKEY: That's all right for you to say! All you have to do is stroll around without a care in the world while I have to carry a heavy pack.

TINKER: Oh, I work, too. And we both have a chance to move about, meeting people and hearing the news. Isn't that better than staying on a farm, plowing the same field and talking to the same three people day after day?

DONKEY: I suppose so. *(Looks around)* Here we come to a village.

TINKER: I can see that you are in a bad mood this morning, Donkey. Cheer up! Things aren't that bad. Who knows what the day will bring? (*Tinker and Donkey stop at center. Tinker shouts in a loud, singsong voice.*) Any rags, any bottles, any bones today? Scissors sharpened! Knives ground! Pots and pans mended! I buy old rags, old bottles, old bones! (*He takes pack off Donkey's back and sets it on the ground. He takes small grindstone and iron kettle out of pack. Terry enters carrying hoe, goes up to Tinker.*)

TERRY: Good morning, tinker.

TINKER: Good morning, lad.

TERRY: Can you use a boy to travel with you and help you, and learn to be a tinker?

TINKER (*Doubtfully*): Well, I don't know. What is your name, lad?

TERRY: My name is Terry, sir.

TINKER: You are a likely-looking lad, Terry, and could make a good tinker, if you tried.

TERRY: Then you'll take me?

TINKER (*Shaking head*): No, my lad, I'm sorry. I have a young nephew, Tim, who is lame. There are many things Tim cannot do, but he could be a tinker, and I plan to teach him.

TERRY: But how can Tim walk about the country?

TINKER: I must find a way for him to ride. Someday, in my travels, I'll find someone with a cart to sell or trade. But you must keep trying to learn a trade, Terry. Be your own man.

(*1st Woman enters, carrying a pot and sack. Terry stands back, and watches Tinker.*)

1ST WOMAN: Good morning, tinker. Here is a pot I've been saving for you to mend. (*Hands Tinker pot*)

TINKER: Good morning to you. *(Looks the pot over)* There's many a good soup been cooked in that pot, I'll be bound.

1ST WOMAN: Yes. And there'll be many a good soup to come, if you can fix it.

TINKER: It can be fixed, and it will still be a better pot than you can buy today. I've heard there's a new ironmonger in the next village who makes good wares, but I've not seen his work.

2ND WOMAN: That would be Jock. He's an honest lad, and will do a good job of work at anything he tries. *(Tinker finishes mending pot, looks it over, and gives it to 1st Woman.)*

TINKER: There you are, ma'am. That should serve you for a good long time.

1ST WOMAN: Thank you, tinker. What do I owe you?

TINKER: Fourpence would be about right.

1st Woman: And cheap enough, too. I don't have fourpence, but here is a sack of potatoes. They should be worth fourpence. (*Donkey stamps feet impatiently as Tinker takes sack. 2nd Woman enters, carrying basket.*)

Tinker: Thank you. One can always eat potatoes.

2nd Woman (*Stepping forward*): Here are some knives to sharpen, tinker.

Tinker: I'll gladly sharpen them. (*He takes knives and pretends to sharpen them on his grindstone. As he works, Boy, carrying kettle and sack, and Girl with wooden doll enter right. Two Men enter left. All gather around Tinker.*) A dull knife can be as dangerous as a sharp one, you know. (*Mike rushes in right. Terry ducks down behind others, and exits quickly.*)

Mike: Has anyone seen that good-for-nothing lad, Terry?

1st Man: And where should Terry be, Mike?

Mike (*Angrily*): Hoeing beans in my field—that's where he should be!

2nd Man: Maybe that's where he is.

Mike: I doubt it!

Tinker: And what is this Terry to you, sir?

Mike: He is a boy I keep out of the kindness of my heart, because he belongs to no one. And a great worry he is, with his hungry mouth and his shiftless ways.

Tinker: Then why not take him to young Jock, the ironmonger in the next village? He may need a boy.

2nd Man: Aye. Jock is looking for a likely boy.

Mike: I may do that. The boy will never make a farmer! (*Stomps off*)

Tinker (*To 2nd Woman*): Now, here are your knives, ma'am. Be careful. Very sharp they are. (*Hands them to 2nd Woman*)

2nd Woman: Thank you, tinker. How much do I owe you?

Tinker: Sixpence, all told.

2ND WOMAN: I have no money, but here are some cabbages that should be worth sixpence. (*Hands him cabbages from basket*)

TINKER: Thank you ma'am. (*Donkey stamps.*)

BOY: My mother wants to know if you can mend her kettle. All she has to pay is this bag of apples. (*Tinker takes kettle and examines it.*)

TINKER: I guess I can do it. It isn't a very big hole. (*Starts to work on kettle*)

1ST MAN: How is haying around the country coming on, tinker?

TINKER: It looks like a good crop this year, but with all the rain, hard to dry. It doesn't do to put green hay in a barn, or even in a haycock. The hay heats up and may catch on fire. Why, only last week such a thing happened to Jim Kelly. His barn was filled with green hay and it caused a fire.

2ND MAN: What a terrible thing!

TINKER (*Handing kettle to Boy*): Here you are, my lad.

BOY: Thank you, tinker. (*Takes kettle, but stays to watch*)

GIRL: My doll has a broken leg, tinker. Can you fix her? (*Tinker looks at doll, hunts through his pockets.*)

TINKER: Well, that's not bad. (*He works on doll.*) I'll make a little hole here, and one here. Now a bit of wire to fasten it together, and here she is. She can bend her knee now. (*Hands doll back*)

GIRL: Oh, thank you, tinker. Here is a pretty pebble for you. It is my good luck pebble.

TINKER (*Taking pebble*): Thank you. It is a very pretty pebble. (*Donkey stamps.*)

BOY'S MOTHER (*Rushing in*): So here you are! I've been waiting for that kettle! (*Takes Boy by ear and leads him offstage. Tinker starts to pack up his things.*)

1ST MAN: I'd better go, or my wife will be after me by the ear. *(As he exits)* Come again soon, tinker. You always bring us news.

2ND MAN: 'Twas a good thing you did for young Terry. I'll put in a good word with Jock for the boy myself. Now I must be off, too. Goodbye, tinker. *(He exits followed by Girl and Women.)*

TINKER *(Waving)*: Goodbye. *(Old Woman hobbles on, carrying kettle.)*

OLD WOMAN *(In a quavering voice)*: Can you fix my kettle, tinker?

TINKER *(Examining kettle)*: Now, that is as old as I have ever seen, but still, a good kettle. Yes, I can fix it.

OLD WOMAN: Many a year has that kettle hung in the fireplace, and strange stories it could tell. *(Tinker works on kettle and soon finishes.)*

TINKER: Here is your kettle, Mother.

OLD WOMAN: Bless you, tinker. It has been many a year since anyone called me "Mother." "Old Hag Blakewell," but never "Mother."

TINKER: The more shame to them for their bad manners, Mother.

OLD WOMAN *(Taking kettle and looking it over)*: Now that is a fine job of mending. I can see that you are no ordinary tinker.

TINKER: Thank you. That will be fourpence.

OLD WOMAN: I have no money to pay you, tinker, but you have been so kind to a poor old woman that I will give you a special gift. *(She takes a green glass ball from her pocket and hands it to Tinker. Donkey stomps and sniffs loudly.)*

TINKER *(Holding up ball)*: This is very pretty, Mother, but neither my donkey nor I can eat it.

OLD WOMAN: Ah, but this is a magic ball, and better than food.

TINKER (*Sighing*): I know of nothing better than food.

OLD WOMAN: Hold this magic ball in your hand and make a wish—and one wish only—for the thing you want most in the world, and that wish will come true.

TINKER: Oh, I don't believe it.

OLD WOMAN: It is true. The fairies made this ball many years ago and gave it to a mortal. Since then, it has passed from person to person, each one making one wish. I was the last to have it, and now it will be yours.

TINKER: Why didn't you wish for gold when you had the chance, Mother? Then you could be paying me now.

OLD WOMAN: Alas, I wished my one wish when I was young, and it was not a kind or a generous wish and little good it did me. Think well before you wish and perhaps you will fare better than I. And remember, wishes can be dangerous. No good comes from them, unless you make the wish for someone else. (*She exits.*)

TINKER (*Watching her exit*): Well, Donkey, now we have a green glass ball, and one wish.

DONKEY (*Crossly*): And much good may it do us. (*Curtain*)

SCENE 2

Time: **A SHORT WHILE LATER**

Setting: **A COUNTRY ROAD. SCENE IS PLAYED BEFORE CURTAIN.**

At Rise: Tinker and Donkey enter right and walk to center.

TINKER: It's been a good day, Donkey. Jock the ironmonger will take young Terry, we will be getting home early, and a fine lot of business we did today!

DONKEY: If you call it business—listening to a lot of chatterboxes.

TINKER: Everyone brought me something to mend and sharpen.

DONKEY: Yes, and not so much as one tuppence in the lot of them.

TINKER: They all gave me something—potatoes, apples, cabbages—

DONKEY (*In disgust*): And the green glass ball! That was the most useless thing of all!

TINKER: I'm not sure of that.

DONKEY: Well, I am. Pray, what am I to eat tonight?

TINKER: There is plenty of grass to eat, and I know you always like a fine red apple.

DONKEY: You should have kept the old woman's kettle, and exchanged it for oats for me.

TINKER: Donkey, you have been complaining all day. Look—here comes Tim to meet us. Be done with your complaints. (*Tim enters. He pats Donkey on head and smiles at Tinker.*)

TIM: Donkey, I suppose you and Uncle have been quarreling. What is it this time?

DONKEY: The usual thing. I can't teach him anything. He works for nothing. Today, we did not even take in one coin.

TINKER: But we did a good day's work, and we are better off than we were this morning. Besides, we have a magic ball.

TIM: A magic ball?

TINKER: See how beautiful it is, and how the light shines through it. *(Holds up ball)*

DONKEY: Humph! You said yourself that we can't eat it.

TINKER: True enough! But something beautiful is worth any price.

TIM: How did you get it?

TINKER: An old woman gave it to me for mending her kettle. She said I must hold it in my hand and make a wish—only one wish—for the thing I want most in the world, and it will come true.

TIM: Are you going to try it?

TINKER: Indeed, I am! I have been waiting for you to help me! Now what shall I wish for?

TIM: Don't you think you should put the ball down until you are ready to wish, Uncle? It would be too bad to wish by accident.

TINKER: True enough. *(Donkey sits in front of curtain opening. Tinker places the ball in front of him.)*

TIM: What do you want the most?

DONKEY: Why don't you wish for a lot of money? Then you could buy me oats every day.

TINKER: Money isn't everything. Why don't I wish for a fine cart?

DONKEY: So I can pull it around the country, I suppose. No, thank you.

TINKER: If you are so smart, what would you have me wish for?

DONKEY: Why don't you wish to be a king? Then I could be the king's donkey. I could have a fine stable to live in, and grooms to care for me. What a life!

TINKER: What a life indeed! A king has many worries. He may live in a fine palace, with many servants, and fine food, but a king can never be sure who his friends are. That is a stupid wish, Donkey. *(Tinker picks up the ball and watches the light shine on it.)*

DONKEY *(Angrily)*: So now you say I am stupid! I don't know what you would do without me to help you. If it were not for me, you would starve! Stupid, indeed!

TINKER *(Angrily to Donkey)*: I have listened to your scolding all this day. I wish you were at the ends of the earth! *(There is a crash, then a bang. Donkey disappears through opening of curtain.)*

TIM: Oh, Uncle! What have you done?

TINKER: I didn't mean it! I forgot that the ball was in my hands. How could I know that the wish would really come true? 'Twas only a little old woman who said so! What can I do?

TIM (Slowly): Do you think I could have a wish?

TINKER: I don't know why not.

TIM: Then I will wish for donkey to be back.

TINKER: Oh, Tim! 'Twould please me greatly to have the donkey back, cross as he is, sometimes. But what about you? Would you not like to be cured of your lameness?

TIM: I would rather have the donkey back, and see you happy again, Uncle. Let me give my wish to you and the donkey. (Tinker gives ball to Tim, who places it carefully on the ground.)

TINKER: Wish carefully then, Tim. (Puts ball into Tim's hands, and leans forward, anxiously)

TIM (Slowly): I wish the tinker's little donkey back, alive and well! (There is a crash, then a bang, and Donkey bursts through the curtains.)

DONKEY (Angrily): What a trick to play on your faithful donkey! How could you be so thoughtless! Now you have wasted your wish!

TIM: But, donkey, we used my wish to bring you back. If you are going to be so bad-tempered, we shall be sorry that we didn't leave you at the ends of the earth. (Donkey hangs his head.)

TINKER: Oh, my poor little Donkey! How glad I am to have you back! Are you all right?

DONKEY (Thoughtfully): Yes, I guess I'm all right. It's too bad we lost the wishes. It was my fault. I complained too much.

TINKER: It was my fault. I lost my temper. *(Tinker hugs Donkey.)*

TIM: What are you going to do with the ball now, Uncle?

TINKER: It isn't any good to us anymore, and somehow it doesn't seem beautiful to me now. I'll toss it away. *(Starts to throw ball away)*

TIM: Wait, Uncle! Suppose someone finds it and makes a terrible wish!

DONKEY: Or a careless wish, not knowing it would come true?

TINKER: I didn't think of that. This magic ball could cause a lot of trouble. I'll smash it.

TIM: But what if each piece is magic? There might be millions of terrible wishes made.

DONKEY: That would be worse than ever! What can we do with it? *(They all think.)*

OLD WOMAN *(Calling from behind curtain)*: Tinker! Tinker! *(Old Woman enters.)* Oh, tinker! Such a time as I've had! Are you all right?

TINKER: Yes, I'm all right. But how did you find me? How did you get here?

OLD WOMAN: Never mind that. I've come to stop you from making a bad wish. I've been worried ever since I gave you that ball.

TINKER *(Sadly)*: It's too late, Mother. I wished foolishly. If I had only wished for the cart, Tim could go with us when we travel.

OLD WOMAN: But no one was hurt by your foolish wish?

TINKER: No. Tim made a wish that fixed everything.

OLD WOMAN: What's done is done! Give me the ball. *(Tinker hands ball to Old Woman.)*

TINKER: And what will you do with it?

Old Woman: It is a dangerous thing. I know a place, far from here, where there is a deep bog, filled with quicksand. I will drop the ball in the middle of that quicksand.

Donkey: When you drop the ball into the quicksand, it will drop out of sight forever.

Old Woman: Yes, but it will not soon be forgotten. This green glass ball has taught us a good lesson: Never make a mean wish. When you wish for something, make it a kind wish, a generous wish. *(She exits as curtain falls.)*

The End

TRICKSTER TALES

HOW BEAR LOST HIS TAIL

an Iroquois tale retold by Joseph Bruchac

Back in the old days, Bear had a tail that was his proudest possession. It was long and black and glossy, and Bear used to wave it around just so that people would look at it. Fox saw this. Fox, as everyone knows, is a trickster and likes nothing better than fooling others. So it was that he decided to play a trick on Bear.

It was the time of year when Hatho, the Spirit of Frost, had swept across the land, covering the lakes with ice and pounding on the trees with his big hammer. Fox made a hole in the ice, right near a place where Bear liked to walk. By the time Bear came by, all around Fox, in a big circle, were big trout and fat perch. Just as Bear was about to ask Fox what he was doing, Fox twitched his tail, which he had sticking through that hole in the ice, and pulled out a huge trout.

"Greetings, Brother," said Fox. "How are you this fine day?"

"Greetings," answered Bear, looking at the big circle of fat fish. "I am well, Brother. But what are you doing?"

"I am fishing," answered Fox. "Would you like to try?"

"Oh, yes," said Bear, as he started to lumber over to Fox's fishing hole.

But Fox stopped him. "Wait, Brother," he said. "This place will not be good. As you can see, I have already caught all the fish. Let us make you a new fishing spot where you can catch many big trout."

Bear agreed, and so he followed Fox to the new place, a place where, as Fox knew very well, the lake was too shallow to catch the winter fish, which always stay in the deepest water when Hatho has covered their ponds. Bear watched as Fox made the hole in the ice, already tasting the fine fish he would soon catch. "Now," said Fox, "you must do just as I tell you. Clear your mind of all thoughts of fish. Do not even think of a song or the fish will hear you. Turn your back to the hole and place your tail inside it. Soon a fish will come and grab your tail and you can pull him out."

"But how will I know if a fish has grabbed my tail if my back is turned?" asked Bear.

"I will hide over here where the fish cannot see me," said Fox. "When a fish grabs your tail, I will shout. Then you must pull as hard as you can to catch your fish. But you must be very patient. Do not move at all until I tell you."

Bear nodded, "I will do exactly as you say." He sat down next to the hole, placed his long beautiful black tail in the icy water, and turned his back.

Fox watched for a time to make sure that Bear was doing as he was told and then, very quietly, sneaked back to his own house and went to bed. The next morning he woke up and thought of Bear. "I wonder if he is still there," Fox said to himself. "I'll just go and check."

So Fox went back to the ice-covered pond, and what do you think he saw? He saw what looked like a little white hill in the middle of the ice. It had snowed during the night and covered Bear, who had fallen asleep while waiting for Fox to

tell him to pull out his tail and catch a fish. And Bear was snoring. His snores were so loud that the ice was shaking. It was so funny that Fox rolled with laughter. But when he was through laughing, he decided the time had come to wake up poor Bear. He crept very close to Bear's ear, took a deep breath, and then shouted: "Now, Bear!!!"

Bear woke up with a start and pulled his long tail as hard as he could. But his tail had been caught in the ice that had frozen over during the night, and as he pulled, it broke off—*Whack!*—just like that. Bear turned around to look at the fish he had caught and instead saw his long, lovely tail caught in the ice.

"Ohhh," he moaned, "ohhh, Fox, I will get you for this." But Fox, even though he was laughing fit to kill, was still faster than Bear and he leaped aside and was gone.

So it is that even to this day, Bears have short tails and no love at all for Fox. And if you ever hear a Bear moaning, it is probably because he remembers the trick Fox played on him long ago and he is mourning for his lost tail.

FROM TIGER TO ANANSI

retold by Philip Sherlock

Once upon a time, and a long, long time ago, the Tiger was king of the forest.

At evening when all the animals sat together in a circle and talked and laughed together, Snake would ask, "Who is the strongest of us all?"

"Tiger is the strongest," cried the dog. "When Tiger whispers the trees listen. When Tiger is angry and cries out, the trees tremble."

"And who is the weakest of all?" asked Snake.

"Anansi," shouted Dog, and they all laughed together, "Anansi the spider is weakest of all. When he whispers no one listens. When he shouts everyone laughs."

Now one day the weakest and strongest came face to face, Anansi and Tiger. They met in a clearing of the forest. The frogs hiding under the cool leaves saw them. The bright green parrots in the branches heard them.

When they met, Anansi bowed so low that his forehead touched the ground. Tiger did not greet him. Tiger just looked at Anansi.

"Good morning, Tiger," cried Anansi. "I have a favor to ask."

"And what is it, Anansi?" said Tiger.

"Tiger, we all know that you are strongest of us all. This is why we give your name to many things. We have Tiger lilies, and Tiger stories, and Tiger moths, and Tiger this and Tiger that. Everyone knows that I am weakest of all. This is why nothing bears my name. Tiger, let something be called after the weakest one so that men may know my name, too."

"Well," said Tiger, without so much as a glance toward Anansi, "what would you like to bear your name?"

"The stories," cried Anansi. "The stories that we tell in the forest at evening time when the sun goes down, the stories about Br'er Snake and Br'er Tacumah, Br'er Cow and Br'er Bird, and all of us."

Now Tiger liked these stories and he meant to keep them as Tiger stories. He thought to himself, "How stupid, how weak this Anansi is. I will play a trick on him so that all the animals will laugh at him." Tiger moved his tail slowly from side to side and said, "Very good, Anansi, very good. I will let the stories be named after you, if you do what I ask."

"Tiger, I will do what you ask."

"Yes, I am sure you will, I am sure you will," said Tiger, moving his tail slowly from side to side. "It is a little thing that I ask. Bring me Mr. Snake alive. Do you know Snake who lives down by the river, Anansi? Bring him to me alive and you can have the stories."

Tiger stopped speaking. He did not move his tail. He looked at Anansi and waited for him to speak. All the animals in the forest waited. Mr. Frog beneath the cool leaves, Mr. Parrot up in the tree, all watched Anansi. They were all ready to laugh at him.

"Tiger, I will do what you ask," said Anansi. At these words a great wave of laughter burst from the forest. The frogs and parrots laughed. Tiger laughed loudest of all, for how could feeble Anansi catch Snake alive?

Anansi went away. He heard the forest laughing at him from every side.

That was on Monday morning. Anansi sat before his house and thought of plan after plan. At last he hit upon one that could not fail. He would build a Calaban.

On Tuesday morning Anansi built a Calaban. He took a strong vine and made a noose. He hid the vine in the grass. Inside the noose he set some of the berries that Snake loved best. Then he waited. Soon Snake came up the path. He saw the berries and went toward them. He lay across the vine and ate the berries. Anansi pulled at the vine to tighten the noose, but Snake's body was too heavy. Anansi saw that the Calaban had failed.

Wednesday came. Anansi made a deep hole in the ground. He made the sides slippery with grease. In the bottom he put some of the bananas that Snake loved. Then he hid in the bush beside the road and waited.

Snake came crawling down the path toward the river. He was hungry and thirsty. He saw the bananas at the bottom of the hole. He saw that the sides of the hole were slippery. First he wrapped his tail tightly around the trunk of a tree, then he reached down into the hole and ate the bananas. When he was finished he pulled himself up by his tail and crawled away. Anansi had lost his bananas and he had lost Snake, too.

Thursday morning came. Anansi made a Fly Up. Inside the trap he put an egg. Snake came down the path. He was happy this morning, so happy that he lifted his head and a third of his long body from the ground. He just lowered his head, took up the egg in his mouth, and never even touched the trap. The Fly Up could not catch Snake.

What was Anansi to do? Friday morning came. He sat and thought all day. It was no use.

Now it was Saturday morning. This was the last day. Anansi went for a walk down by the river. He passed by the hole where Snake lived. There was Snake, his body hidden in the hole, his head resting on the ground at the entrance to the hole. It was early morning. Snake was watching the sun rise above the mountains.

"Good morning, Anansi," said Snake.

"Good morning, Snake," said Anansi.

"Anansi, I am very angry with you. You have been trying to catch me all week. You set a Fly Up to catch me. The day before you made a Slippery Hole for me. The day before that you made a Calaban. I have a good mind to kill you, Anansi."

"Ah, you are too clever, Snake," said Anansi. "You are much too clever. Yes, what you say is so. I tried to catch you, but I failed. Now I can never prove that you are the longest animal in the world, longer even than the bamboo tree."

"Of course I am the longest of all animals," cried Snake. "I am much longer than the bamboo tree."

"What, longer than that bamboo tree across there?" asked Anansi.

"Of course I am," said Snake. "Look and see." Snake came out of the hole and stretched himself out at full length.

"Yes, you are very, very long," said Anansi, "but the bamboo tree is very long, too. Now that I look at you and at the bamboo tree, I must say that the bamboo tree seems longer. But it's hard to say because it is farther away."

"Well, bring it nearer," cried Snake. "Cut it down and put it beside me. You will soon see that I am much longer."

Anansi ran to the bamboo tree and cut it down. He placed it on the ground and cut off all its branches. Bush, bush, bush, bush! There it was, long and straight as a flagstaff.

"Now put it beside me," said Snake.

Anansi put the long bamboo tree down on the ground beside Snake. Then he said: "Snake, when I go up to see where your head is, you will crawl up. When I go down to see where your tail is, you will crawl down. In that way you will always seem to be longer than the bamboo tree, which really is longer than you are."

"Tie my tail, then!" said Snake. "Tie my tail! I know that I am longer than the bamboo, whatever you say."

Anansi tied Snake's tail to the end of the bamboo. Then he ran up to the other end.

"Stretch, Snake, stretch, and we will see who is longer."

A crowd of animals were gathering round. Here was something better than a race. "Stretch, Snake, stretch," they called.

Snake stretched as hard as he could. Anansi tied him around his middle so that he should not slip back. Now one more try. Snake knew that if he stretched hard enough, he would prove to be longer than the bamboo.

Anansi ran up to him. "Rest yourself for a little, Snake, and then stretch again. If you can stretch another six inches you will be longer than the bamboo. Try your hardest. Stretch so that you even have to shut your eyes. Ready?"

"Yes," said Snake. Then Snake made a mighty effort. He stretched so hard that he had to squeeze his eyes shut. "Hooray!" cried the animals. "You are winning, Snake. Just two inches more."

And at that moment Anansi tied Snake's head to the bamboo. There he was. At last he had caught Snake, all by himself.

The animals fell silent. Yes, there Snake was, all tied up, ready to be taken to Tiger. And feeble Anansi had done this. They could laugh at him no more.

And never again did Tiger dare to call these stories by his own name. They were Anansi stories forever after, from that day to this.

BRER RABBIT GETS
BRER FOX'S DINNER

retold by Julius Lester

If you ain't never heard about Brer Rabbit and Brer Fox, you might get the idea from these stories that they are enemies. Well, that ain't the way it is. On the other hand they weren't friends either. Brer Rabbit was Brer Rabbit, which meant he couldn't help it if he woke up some mornings and the first thing he thought about was creating devilment. And Brer Fox was Brer Fox. Wasn't his fault if he woke up thinking about the same thing. So they weren't enemies and they weren't friends. They were who they were. Another way of putting it is: They ain't who they wasn't. Now that that's all clear, let's get on with the story.

Not having anything better or worse to do one day, Brer Rabbit decided to see what Brer Fox was up to. As he got close to Brer Fox's house, he heard a lot of hammering. When he got there, he saw Brer Fox on the roof nailing shingles as fast as he could.

Well, Brer Rabbit treated work like he did his mamma, and he wouldn't hit his mamma a lick. So he looked around to see what else he could see, and there by the fence post was Brer Fox's dinner pail. Brer Rabbit knew there was more food in it than there was in his stomach. That didn't seem right. How was he going to get Brer Fox's dinner from where it wasn't doing no good to where it would do a whole lot of good?

"Brer Fox! How you doing today?" Brer Rabbit called up.

"Busy. Ain't got time to be flapping gums with you."

"What are you doing up there?"

"Putting on a new roof before winter come."

"You need some help?"

"I do, but where am I going to get it at?"

"I'm a powerful man with a hammer, Brer Fox. I'll give you a hand."

Brer Rabbit climbed up to the roof and set to work. Pretty soon he was out-hammering Brer Fox. He was putting roofing on like winter was on the outskirts of town. He nailed and nailed and nailed until he was right up to Brer Fox's tail.

Brer Rabbit pushed the tail to one side, but, a tail being a tail, it just swished right back.

"Don't know how come some folks got to have such long tails," Brer Rabbit mumbled to himself.

He brushed the tail aside again and resumed nailing. He nailed under Brer Fox. He nailed around Brer Fox. He nailed beside Brer Fox. He nailed and he nailed until all of a sudden Brer Fox dropped his hammer and let out a yell, "Ow! Brer Rabbit! You done nailed my tail!"

Brer Rabbit looked at him, eyes big. "I done what? You got to be joking, Brer Fox. Don't be accusing me of something I ain't done."

Brer Fox hollered and squalled and kicked and squealed. "Have mercy, Brer Rabbit! Unnail my tail! Unnail my tail!"

Brer Rabbit started down the ladder, shaking his head. "I must be losing my aim, my stroke, or something. Maybe my eyes is getting weak. I ain't never nailed nobody's tail before.

Doing something like that upsets me. Doing something like that upsets me so much, it makes me hungry."

All the while Brer Fox is hollering and screaming and squalling.

Brer Rabbit climbed down the ladder, still muttering to himself about how getting upset made him hungry. He opened up Brer Fox's dinner pail and helped himself to the fried chicken, corn, and biscuits inside. When he finished, he wiped his mouth on his coattail, belched a time or two, and went on down the road, hoping he hadn't done no permanent damage to Brer Fox's long, pretty tail.

BRER RABBIT GOES BACK
TO MR. MAN'S GARDEN
retold by Julius Lester

Mr. Man's garden was too delicious-looking for Brer Rabbit to leave alone. And anyway, it wasn't right for Mr. Man to have all them pretty vegetables to himself. Obviously, he didn't believe in sharing. Being worried about Mr. Man's soul, Brer Rabbit decided he'd make Mr. Man share.

A few mornings later Mr. Man went to town. As he was leaving he hollered to his daughter, "Janey! Don't you let Brer Rabbit get in my green peas. You hear me?"

"Yes, Daddy," she said.

Brer Rabbit was hiding in the bushes, listening. Soon as Mr. Man left, Brer Rabbit walked up to the little girl as bold as day.

"Ain't you Janey?" he asked.

"My daddy call me Janey. What your daddy call you?"

"Well, my daddy dead, but when he was living he called me Billy Malone." He smiled. "I passed your daddy in the road and he said for me to come tell you to give me some sparrow grass."

Janey had been warned against Brer Rabbit, but not Billy Malone, so she opened the gate and let Brer Rabbit into the garden. Brer Rabbit got as much sparrow grass as he could carry and left.

Mr. Man came back and saw that somebody had been in his garden. He asked Janey about it. She told him that Billy

Malone said it was all right for him to go in and get some sparrow grass. Mr. Man knew something was up but didn't say anything.

Next morning when he got ready to go, he told Janey to keep an eye out for Brer Rabbit and not let anyone get any sparrow grass.

When Mr. Man was out of sight, Brer Rabbit come walking down the road and greeted the little girl, bowing low like a real gentleman. "I saw your daddy just now. He said I couldn't have no sparrow grass today, but it would be all right if I helped myself to the English peas."

The little girl opened the gate and Brer Rabbit made off with enough English peas to feed all of England.

When Mr. Man came back, his pea vines looked like a storm had hit 'em, and he was hot! "Who been in my peas?" he asked his daughter.

"Mr. Billy Malone," she said.

"What this Billy Malone look like?"

"He got a split lip, pop eyes, big ears, and a bobtail, Daddy."

Mr. Man didn't have a bit of trouble recognizing that description. He fixed a box trap and set it in the garden among the peanuts. The next morning he told Janey, "Now, whatever you do today, don't let nobody have any sparrow grass, and don't let 'em get any more English peas, the few I got left."

Soon as Mr. Man was out of sight, here come Brer Rabbit. He bowed low and said, "Good morning, Miz Janey. I met your daddy down the road there and he said I can't have no more sparrow grass or English peas, but to help myself to the peanuts."

Janey let him in the garden. Brer Rabbit headed straight for the peanut patch, where he tripped the string and the box fell right on top of him. He was caught and he knew it.

Wasn't long before Mr. Man came back. He went to the peanut patch and saw the overturned box. He stooped down, peered through the slats, and saw Brer Rabbit inside, quivering.

Mr. Man whooped. "Yes, sir! I got you this time, you devil! I got you! And when I get through with you, ain' gon' be nothing left. I'm gon' carry your foot in my pocket, put your meat in the pot, and wear your fur on my head."

Words like that always put a chill up and down Brer Rabbit's spine. "Mr. Man, I know I done wrong. And if you let me go, I promise I'll stay away from your garden."

Mr. Man chuckled. "You gon' stay away from my garden if I don't let you go too. I got to go to the house to get my butcher knife."

Mr. Man went to the house, but he forgot to close the garden gate behind him. Brer Fox came down the road, and seeing the open gate, took it as an invitation and walked on in. He heard something hollering and making a lot of racket. He wandered around until he found the noise coming from underneath a box. "What the dickens is that?" he asked.

Brer Rabbit would've known that voice anywhere. "Run, Brer Fox! Run! Get out of here right now if you care about your life!"

"What's wrong, Brer Rabbit?"

"Mr. Man trapped me in here and is making me eat lamb. I'm about to bust wide open I done ate so much lamb. Run, Brer Fox, before he catch you."

Brer Fox wasn't thinking about running. "How's the lamb?"

"It tastes good at first, but enough is enough and too much is plenty. You better get out of here before he catches you."

Brer Fox wasn't running anywhere. "I like lamb, Brer Rabbit." He took the box off Brer Rabbit. "Put the box over me." Brer Rabbit did so gladly and decided not to wait around for the next chapter.

The story don't say what happened to Brer Fox. Brer Rabbit took care of himself. Now it's up to Brer Fox to take care of himself. That's the name of that tune.

STORIES FROM THE BIBLE

NOAH AND THE ARK

Long, long ago, when the world was still young, the people had already turned wicked. They fought all the time. They lied and cheated. The strong put down the weak. The rich robbed the poor. There was neither peace nor safety anywhere.

When God saw the wickedness of the people, he began to think it would have been better if he had never made them in the first place.

But in all this wickedness, there was one man who was good and true. His name was Noah. He had a wife, and they had three sons.

Noah often told his neighbors how wrong it was to do as they were doing. He warned them that if they did not change their ways, some great disaster would surely happen. But they only laughed at him and kept on in their wickedness as before.

One day, Noah and his three sons set to work chopping trees and shaping them into planks. The neighbors looked on and jeered. "What are you doing?" they asked.

"We are building an ark," Noah answered quietly.

"Ha, ha! Who ever did so foolish a thing as to build a boat on a hilltop a hundred miles from the sea? Noah, you have lost your senses."

"I am doing as the Lord has told me," said Noah. "He is angry with you because of your wickedness. He is going to send a great flood of waters that will rise till it sweeps away every living thing on the earth. He has told me to build this ark so that I and my family may be saved, as well as the creatures we take with us."

The people laughed and jeered all the more. And instead of helping, they tried to hinder him. But Noah and his sons ignored them and kept working. They built the ark as God had told them.

When it was finished, the ark was almost five hundred feet long and three stories high. It had only one door and one window.

They covered the whole ark with a roof and began to stock it with food. They put in not only food for themselves, but also a great supply of hay, grain, roots, and fruit of every sort. Then they went out into the woods and fields and brought together all the wild and tame animals they could find. They brought two of every kind of animal, all the beasts of the field and birds of the air and things that creep on the ground.

It must have been a strange sight to see these creatures marching up the hill and boarding the ark, two by two. They went quietly into the great boat, as if they knew that it was the only safe place for them. The lions did not quarrel with the tigers, and the sheep were not afraid of the wolves. Each one took the place that had been set apart for it in the ark. All were as peaceful and kind as though they were members of the same happy family.

When the last of the creatures was safely on board, Noah and his wife entered, followed by his three sons and their wives. They shut the door behind them. And then it began to rain. And it rained and rained and rained.

For forty days and forty nights, the rain came down without stopping. The sea was filled to overflowing, and the water covered the land until even the tops of the mountains were hidden.

Nothing survived in the angry waters of the flood. But the great ark floated on the waters, and the eight good people and the living creatures in it were kept safe and alive.

At last there came a great wind to drive back the waters.

The ark settled on the top of a high mountain called Ararat. Noah opened the window and let a raven fly out. The raven flew back and forth, but there was no dry land in sight.

By and by Noah sent out a dove. The dove could find nothing to eat, nor any safe place to rest, so at last it returned to the ark.

A week later, Noah sent out the dove again. This time it returned bearing in its beak an olive branch with new green leaves.

Noah knew that the worst was over. But he waited another week and then sent the dove out again. This time it did not return, for now the fields were dry and the bird could find plenty of food and a place to build a nest.

Noah waited yet longer in the ark until the Lord told him to go forth. Then they opened wide the door of the ark. All went out, making their way down the steep mountainside to the green and pleasant plains below. And the beasts and the birds and the creeping things went out also, two by two, and scattered far and wide across the land.

When Noah and his family reached the foot of the mountain, they saw the meadows dotted with flowers and the trees already laden with fruit. Their hearts were filled with thankfulness to God. And as they prayed, they heard a voice saying, "I will never punish my world with such a flood again. So long as the earth remains, seedtime and harvest, and summer and winter, and day and night shall not cease."

Then, looking up, Noah saw a rainbow like a mighty bridge between heaven and earth. And this, he knew, was a sign of God's loving promise.

JOSEPH AND HIS BROTHERS

1

Long ago, in the land of Canaan, there lived a wealthy man named Jacob. He had hundreds and hundreds of sheep and cattle. He had droves of camels and donkeys. But he knew that what made him truly rich were his twelve strong sons. While Jacob loved all his sons, he loved the one called Joseph best of all. To show his pride in the boy, Jacob gave Joseph a coat of many colors. But when Joseph's older brothers saw that he was their father's favorite, they grew jealous of him.

One day Joseph had a dream. He told it to his brothers.

"Behold," he said, "we were binding sheaves in the field. My sheaf arose and stood upright. And your sheaves stood round about, and bowed to my sheaf."

Joseph told his brothers this dream without thinking how they might feel about it. His jealous brothers saw a meaning in the dream. "Do you think you will rule over us someday, little brother?" they said angrily.

Soon after this Joseph's brothers went to find new pastures for their flocks some miles away from their home. Jacob sent Joseph to see how his brothers were getting along and bring him word.

When Joseph's brothers saw him coming, they made up their minds to kill him. "Behold, here comes the dreamer," they said to one another. "Let us slay him and cast him into a pit, and say some evil beast devoured him."

Meanwhile, Joseph came to where his brothers were. At once, they grabbed him, pulled off his coat of many colors, and threw him into a deep, empty pit. Then the heartless brothers sat down to eat their meal, ignoring Joseph's piteous cries.

While they ate, a caravan approached. It was a band of merchants with their camels laden with spices and myrrh. They were on their way south to Egypt.

Upon seeing the caravan, the brother named Judah asked, "What good does it do us to kill our brother? Instead, let us sell him to these merchants."

This plan satisfied them all. So they drew Joseph out of the pit and sold him to the merchants for twenty pieces of silver. Then they killed a goat and dipped Joseph's coat in its blood. Later, they took the coat to their father and said, "This have we found."

The poor father cried, "It is my son's coat. An evil beast has devoured him. Joseph was surely torn to pieces." Jacob wept. He tore his clothes, put on rough mourning robes of sackcloth, and would not be comforted.

But Joseph was alive. Day by day, he trudged along beside the camels of the caravan under the hot, cloudless sky. At last the palm trees that border the river Nile came into sight. Joseph had come to the land of Egypt.

2

Egypt at that time—more than four thousand years ago—was the greatest and richest country in the world. As the caravan wound its way into the rich valley of the Nile, Joseph saw the grand and lofty pyramids.

There, in a dusty marketplace in the shadow of the great pyramids, the merchants sold Joseph as a slave to the captain of the royal guard of Pharaoh, the king of Egypt.

Even though he was now a slave in a strange land, Joseph did not lose heart. Nor did he spend any time grieving about things that could not be helped. He made up his mind to do his best at all times, no matter what might happen to him.

As the years passed by and he grew up to manhood, he proved himself to be so honest and wise that his master trusted him with everything he had. At last, he made Joseph the manager of all his lands and houses and goods.

But the time came when misfortune again befell Joseph. The wife of Joseph's master was a thoughtless, wicked woman. She accused Joseph of things of which he was not guilty, and had him thrown into Pharaoh's prison.

Yet even then Joseph did not lose hope. He was so wise and trustworthy that the jailer soon made him his chief helper.

Some of Pharaoh's servants were also in the prison at that time. One morning, Joseph came to them and noticed they were sad.

"Why do you look so sad today?" he asked.

And they told him, "We have each dreamed a strange dream, but there is no one to tell us what it means."

But with the Lord's help, Joseph told them the meaning of their dreams.

3

Then it happened that the king of Egypt had a strange dream. Pharaoh dreamed that while he stood on the banks of the Nile, there came up out of the river seven fat cattle to feed in a meadow. And there came up after them seven poor, lean cattle. And the seven lean cattle ate the seven fat cattle. But though the seven lean cattle had eaten the fat cattle, they remained as lean as before.

Next, Pharaoh dreamed that he saw seven ears of corn upon one stalk, full and good, and after them seven ears withered and thin. And the seven thin ears devoured the seven good ears.

Pharaoh thought a great deal about his strange dreams. He sent for all the wise men of Egypt and commanded them to tell him the meaning of his dreams. But none of them could explain what the dreams meant.

Then Pharaoh's chief butler came forward. He had been in prison the year before. He remembered that Joseph had given him a true explanation of one of his dreams. So the butler told Pharaoh about Joseph and his great wisdom. "Send for Joseph," said the butler, "and he will interpret your dreams."

Pharaoh called Joseph to the palace and said, "I have had two strange dreams, and the wisest men in my kingdom can not explain them. I am told that you understand such things, and I have sent for you to tell me what they mean."

"The answer is not in me," said Joseph, "but God shall give Pharaoh an answer."

Pharaoh told Joseph about his dreams. Then Joseph said, "Both dreams mean the same thing. The God of my father has sent them to you so that you might know the things that are about to happen in Egypt. The seven fat cattle and the seven full ears of corn mean that there will be seven years of plenty. And the seven lean cattle and the seven thin ears mean seven years of famine."

Joseph advised the king to store food during the seven years of plenty to use during the seven years of famine. He also advised him to find a wise, honest man to be in charge.

Pharaoh took this advice. He appointed Joseph himself to fill the office. He gave Joseph fine clothes and put a gold chain about his neck. He took the ring from his hand and put it on Joseph's. He made Joseph governor over all the land of Egypt. Only Pharaoh himself had more power than Joseph.

The years of plenty came. Joseph gathered grain as the sand of the sea. Then the seven years of famine began, and the people cried out to Pharaoh for bread. Pharaoh told them to go to Joseph. So Joseph opened all the storehouses and sold grain to the Egyptians.

4

The famine spread beyond Egypt. All around, the people knew terrible hunger, especially in Joseph's old home, the land of Canaan, where his father Jacob and his brothers still lived.

Jacob heard that grain could be bought in Egypt. So he told his sons to go down into that country and buy a supply. Ten of Jacob's sons set out for Egypt. But his youngest son, Benjamin, he loved dearly. So he kept the boy at home.

You remember that Joseph was now the governor of Egypt, and it was to him that all who wished to buy grain had to go. So the ten sons of Jacob were brought before Joseph. They bowed themselves to the earth. But they did not recognize him. How could they? They had last seen him a weeping boy. Now they found a man of great power, dressed in royal garments.

Joseph knew his brothers at once. His heart yearned for his own people, but he wished to test his brothers, so he spoke to them roughly. He accused them of being spies. "You say you have a younger brother at home," he sneered. "Bring him here so that I may see if you speak truly."

The brothers knew that their father would grieve if Benjamin were called away. So they refused. Joseph threw them into prison for three days. Then he called them before him again.

He heard his brothers speaking tenderly of their father and of Benjamin. He heard them admit how cruel they had been to him in selling him into slavery. He heard them agree that this punishment had come to them justly for their cruelty.

All this time it was hard for Joseph to keep back his feelings. His brothers did not think that the governor of the land understood what they were saying, for he spoke to them through an interpreter. But Joseph understood it all, and he turned his face from them and wept.

Finally the brothers agreed to bring the boy, Benjamin, into Egypt. Then Joseph filled their sacks with corn, and they trudged home to Canaan.

A hard task was now before the brothers. They had to tell their father that the governor of Egypt had ordered them to return and bring Benjamin with them. This came near breaking the old father's heart. Joseph dead! And now Benjamin was to be taken away! He felt that he could not let him go.

But the famine still lasted. Soon the store of food the brothers had brought from Egypt was gone. They must either starve or go back for more. So Jacob had to let them go and take with them the child of his old age, the little Benjamin.

5

All eleven of Joseph's brothers stood before him and bowed themselves to the earth. Joseph ordered a great feast to be set for them. He asked, "Is your father well, the old man of whom you spoke? Is he alive yet?" They answered that he was alive, and again bowed.

Joseph then lifted up his eyes and saw Benjamin, and said, "And this is your younger brother of whom you spoke to me? God be gracious to thee, my son."

It was even harder for Joseph to keep back his feelings than it had been before. He had to hasten away into his own chamber and weep.

Then Joseph gave orders to the steward of his house. "Fill the men's sacks with food," he said, "as much as they can carry. And put my cup, the silver cup, in the sack of the youngest son."

At dawn the next morning the brothers set out for home. But they had not gone far when they were stopped by Joseph's steward.

The steward said, "Why have you returned evil for good? You have taken my lord's drinking cup!"

"It isn't true!" said the brothers. "And we will prove it. If any of us has taken your master's cup, then he will pay for it with his life."

Each man took down his sack and opened it. Of course, when the steward emptied Benjamin's sack, there glittered the silver cup.

The brothers cried out in terrible distress and hurried back to the city. They threw themselves at Joseph's feet and begged him to let the boy go free.

Judah said, "Please, my lord, our father loves him best of us all. Losing the boy would send him to his grave. Please, sir, let me be your servant in my brother's place."

Then Joseph knew that his brothers' hearts were no more filled with jealousy and selfishness. He cried out to them, "I am Joseph, your brother whom you sold into Egypt. But do not be grieved or angry with yourselves that you sold me, for God sent me before you to save your lives."

And he fell upon his brother Benjamin's neck and wept, and Benjamin wept on his neck. Then the brothers, twelve now, talked together for a long time. At last, Joseph said, "Go, fetch our father and all your families down from Canaan. The best part of Egypt's land shall be yours."

Joseph's family did as he commanded. They journeyed down into Egypt and made their homes there. Then, at last, Jacob held Joseph's children in his arms and blessed them. And there was great happiness between them for the rest of their days.

As for Joseph, he held his high office during all his long life. He was the true king, for he was Pharaoh's wise guide, and made the people happy.

THE STORY OF MOSES

1. MOSES IN THE BULRUSHES

As long as Joseph lived, and for some time after, the people of Israel were treated kindly by the Egyptians. But many years passed, and another pharaoh began to rule over Egypt. He cared nothing for Joseph's people. He said, "The people of Israel are growing too strong. Let us rule them more strictly. Let us heap hard tasks upon them."

And so the Egyptians made the Israelites build cities for them, and give to them a large part of the crops from their fields. But still the people of Israel remained strong and grew in number.

When the pharaoh saw this, he gave a cruel command. He gave orders that every one of the baby boys born to the people of Israel should be thrown into the river and drowned.

When the people of Israel heard this awful command, they cried, "God save us! Send someone to deliver us from this wicked pharaoh of Egypt."

About this time, there was born in the home of one of the Israelites a fine, strong baby boy who had a very loud cry. As he grew larger, his cries grew louder. Finally, when he was three months old, his mother knew she could hide him no longer. Any day the Egyptian soldiers might discover the baby and kill him.

So she made a basket of bulrushes, like a small boat or ark, and rubbed tar and pitch over it to keep the water out. Early one morning she put the baby in the basket and laid it among the tall reeds that grew on the bank of the river. The boy's sister, Miriam, hid behind the reeds so she could watch over her brother and see what became of him.

Not long after, the pharaoh's daughter came down to the water to bathe. As she walked along the riverside, she saw the little basket floating among the reeds.

The princess turned to her handmaidens. She said, "What is in that basket? Go and bring it to me!"

One of her maids ran to fetch the basket. When the princess looked inside, she saw the baby boy. He saw her kind face, but it was not his mother's, and he began to cry.

Compassion filled the princess's heart. She said, "This is one of the Israelite children. Some poor mother has hidden him here. He is a splendid child. I will take him and bring him up as my own son."

Now Miriam ran out of her hiding place. "My lady," she said, "would you like me to find you a nurse to take care of the baby?"

Pharaoh's daughter smiled. "Go," she said.

Miriam ran swiftly to her mother and told her all that had happened. The two hurried back to the princess, and the child was gently placed back in his mother's arms.

"Take care of this child for me and I will give you your wages," said the princess.

So, loved and tended by his own mother, the boy grew up in Pharaoh's palace and was treated like the princess's son. And the princess named the boy Moses, which, in that language of long ago, means "drawn out of the water."

Moses grew up to be a handsome lad, quick, strong, and full of promise. The wisest men in the land were his teachers. They taught him music and math, science and the stars. He was taught to be a brave soldier and a leader of men. It was the wish

of both Pharaoh and his daughter that Moses should become
a great ruler in the land, and stand next to Pharaoh in power.

Still, Moses was often sad and troubled. He saw that while
Pharaoh was kind to him, he was very cruel to the people of
Moses, the Israelites. He saw how they suffered as they labored
under the whip and the hot sun to build the Egyptians' grand
palaces and pyramids.

At last, Moses could bear it no longer. He fled from the
kingdom of Egypt to the far wilderness where there were no
pharaohs and no palaces, only shepherds and their bright
cloth tents.

Out in the wilderness, Moses lived a pleasant life. He
married a lovely girl, tended her father's sheep, and cared no
more to be a prince of Egypt.

2. THE PROMISED LAND

Forty years passed by. Still the Israelites suffered in Egypt. Again and again they cried out, and prayed to God that he would send them help.

Then one day, as Moses was tending a flock of sheep, he saw a strange vision. A bush that stood close by seemed to catch fire. It burned with a blaze as bright as the sun. Yet the bush was not harmed in the least.

Moses thought, "I must turn aside and go see this great sight. With what kind of fire can a bush burn and not be burned up?"

As he stood looking at the burning bush and wondering, he heard a voice call, "Moses! Moses!"

And Moses said, "Here I am." Then he hid his face for fear and listened.

The voice from the burning bush said, "I am the God of your fathers. I have seen the suffering of my people in Egypt and I have heard their cries. I will deliver them out of the hand of the Egyptians. I will bring them to a good, large land, flowing with milk and honey. Come now, and I will send you to Pharaoh so that you may bring the children of Israel out of Egypt."

Moses went back to Egypt with his brother Aaron, and said to Pharaoh, "The God of Israel has come to us. He tells you, 'Let my people go!'"

Pharaoh said, "Who is the God of Israel? Why should I obey his commands? I do not know your God, and I will not let the Israelites go!" And he made the Israelites work harder than ever.

Moses warned Pharaoh that God wanted him to let the Israelites go. But Pharaoh would not listen. So God struck Egypt with nine mighty plagues, each more terrible than the last.

First, all the water in Egypt turned to blood. The fish died, and the Egyptians could not drink. But Pharaoh would not let the Israelites go.

Then frogs, lice, and flies swarmed over the land. The Egyptians' animals grew sick and died. But Pharaoh would not let the Israelites go.

Then hail and locusts destroyed their crops. For three days, a thick darkness blanketed the land. But still Pharaoh would not let the Israelites go.

Then God said to Moses, "I will bring one more plague upon Pharaoh and Egypt, and he will let you go."

Moses went to Pharaoh and said, "At midnight, God will go out into Egypt, and the firstborn of every family in Egypt will die. But none of the Israelites will be harmed, so that you will, at last, know the God of Israel." Moses left Pharaoh in a great anger. But Pharaoh's heart was hardened, and he would not let the Israelites go.

At midnight, God went out into Egypt. God had told the Israelites to mark the doors of their homes with the blood of a lamb, and he would pass over their homes. So God passed over the children of the Israelites, and none of them were harmed. But that night, a terrible cry rose up from the Egyptians, because their firstborn were dead.

Before the sun rose the next morning, Pharaoh called Moses before him. His face was hard as stone, but his eyes were red from weeping: Pharaoh's own son had died during the night.

And Pharaoh said to Moses, "You—and your people—may go."

Quickly, the Israelites gathered all their belongings and fled. God led them out of Egypt as a towering cloud during the day and a pillar of fire at night. After many days, the Israelites stopped to rest by the sea.

But back in Egypt, Pharaoh thought, "The Israelites were our servants! I should not have let them go!" So he called together his army, readied his chariot, and rushed out after the Israelites.

Soon, the Israelites saw the mighty Egyptian army approaching. They were very afraid. What could they do? On one side, Pharaoh's army came charging against them, and on the other side was the sea.

Then God spoke to Moses and said, "Lift up your staff and stretch your hand out over the sea."

Moses did, and God sent a great wind to part the waters. The Israelites hurried along the dry path through the sea, and crossed to the opposite shore. But when Pharaoh's army galloped in after them, God made the waters flood back, and the Egyptian army disappeared beneath the waves.

Moses and the Israelites saw Pharaoh's army destroyed. They knew that finally they were free. Miriam, Moses' sister, took out a tambourine and began to sing. Together, the Israelites sang and danced to celebrate. Then they began their long journey into the desert, back to Canaan, their home and Promised Land.

LIFE STORIES

Louis Pasteur: Battle with Death
by Dorothy Haas

If the people of little Louis Pasteur's village in France had been asked to guess what he would become when he grew up, few would have said he would become one of the world's greatest scientists. "Little Louis...," they would have said thoughtfully. "Well, have you seen any of the pictures he draws? They are really very good. He will probably grow up to be an artist."

Some of the scientist's boyhood drawings still exist. Artists agree that Louis Pasteur, scientist, could have been—Louis Pasteur, artist!

"**R**un for your life!"

"Mad wolf!"

A small boy pushed open the heavy door of his home. He slipped inside, slamming it behind him.

His heart pounding, little Louis Pasteur—for that was the boy's name—turned. He brushed aside the lace curtain on the window next to the door. The scene outside was something out of a nightmare.

A maddened, snarling wolf, foaming at the mouth, charged down the street. Panic-stricken people scattered before it. Some found shelter. Others, not so lucky, were bitten. Little Louis closed his eyes. He pressed his face into the scratchy lace of the curtain. But he could not shut out those dreadful cries.

Soon the howls of the suffering beast faded in the distance. Then they stopped altogether. The wolf had gone back to the dark forests that surrounded Arbois. Silence returned to the tiny town.

Once more Louis dared to look outside. A pitiful parade was passing by. One by one, the wolf's victims were being helped up the street. They seemed to be going to the blacksmith's shop.

Louis pulled open the door and followed them. What he saw there was to haunt him for the rest of his life.

The only known treatment for rabies, caused by the bite of a mad animal, was a fearful one. Each of the wolf's victims— eight in all—was brought into the blacksmith's shop. There the doctor touched a red-hot poker to the wounds. He was trying to burn away the poisons left there by the sick wolf.

But the treatment was useless. In the weeks that followed, the wolf's victims sickened. At last, one by one, they died. There was no cure for rabies.

Many years passed. The little boy of Arbois grew up. He studied chemistry and biology. He became a scientist, an honored scientist known throughout France. In his laboratory he found the answers to many grave problems.

The farmers' sheep and cattle died in great numbers from a certain disease called anthrax. Dr. Louis Pasteur found a way to vaccinate them, and so to keep them healthy.

Many people became ill and died from drinking the milk of sick cows. Dr. Pasteur developed a method of making milk safe. We still use that method today. It is called pasteurization.

Many were the problems that Dr. Pasteur solved. But during the years he could not forget the cries of the terrified townsfolk of Arbois. The trouble was that no one knew quite where to start on the fearful problem of rabies. For nobody knew what caused the disease. Today we know that it is caused by a virus, a germ so small that it cannot be seen under the usual kind of microscope. But Dr. Pasteur did not know this.

One day he was in his laboratory with his assistant. They were talking about rabies, as they often did. The elderly scientist, limping from an illness which had left him painfully crippled, moved up and down the long room as they talked.

"We do not know what causes rabies," he said. He paused for a thoughtful moment, leaning on his cane. "But every problem has an answer," he went on. "And to every answer there is a clue. Let's start looking for a clue. We will begin with the sick animals themselves!"

In the weeks that followed, strange guests came to live in Dr. Pasteur's laboratory in Paris: mad rabbits, mad guinea pigs, mad dogs. The scientist studied the disease in these animals. He even studied the saliva, which he took from their foaming mouths. But he did not find his clue.

He worked long hours. He was in the laboratory, bent over his microscope, long before his assistant opened the door in the morning. And he stayed on, lost in thought, long after his assistant went home at night.

Months went by. Many times Dr. Pasteur thought he had the answer, only to meet with failure. But he did not give up. And then, at last, the long hours of work had their reward.

He injected nerve tissues from sick animals into healthy ones in a certain way. He found that in doing this he could cause rabies in healthy animals. This was because the germs were concentrated in the nerve tissue. And this turned out to be the clue that Dr. Pasteur had been waiting for.

He found that by letting this tissue stand for a few days it became weak. When a dog received this weak nerve tissue it became sick, yes. But not so sick that it died. The dog got well. And after that, even if injected with the strongest nerve tissue, the dog did not develop rabies. Its body had built up strength against the disease. The dog was "immune."

The scientist knew that persons bitten by rabid dogs do not show signs of illness until nearly a month later. If resistance could be built up in these people before they showed signs of the disease, perhaps they might not sicken at all! He worked up a course of treatment. It would take fourteen days.

On the first day a dose of a very weak fourteen-day-old nerve tissue was to be given to a person who had been bitten. This was followed on the second day by a thirteen-day-old dose. And so on, until on the last day strong virus was to be given. During this time the person's body would be building up resistance. Finally, the victim would have so much resistance that he would not get sick.

Dr. Pasteur had found his cure for rabies—or he thought he had. It had been successful with dogs. Would it work as well on a human being? Perhaps it would harm, rather than help, a person who had been bitten!

At last he decided what he would do. He would try the treatment on himself! If he was not harmed by it, then he would be sure that it was safe for everyone.

But something happened before he had a chance to test his cure. It happened on July 6, 1885. Footsteps sounded on the stairway leading to the laboratory. The door was flung open. A woman rushed into the room.

"Dr. Pasteur!" she cried, when she spied the scientist. "I am Madame Meister. I have heard you are working on a cure for rabies. You must help my boy Joseph or he will surely die. We have come all the way from Alsace!"

She turned and pointed to a little boy. He stood in the doorway, smiling shyly at the great scientist. Joseph Meister was nine years old. He had been bitten fourteen times.

Dr. Pasteur stood up, shaking his head. "But, my good woman!" he said. "The treatment has never been tried on a person. It may harm—"

"Please, Doctor!" the woman pleaded. "You are our only hope!"

The scientist was thoughtful. "Let me think," he said. "I will let you know later today."

After Madame Meister and Joseph had gone, the scientist sat down at his desk. Should he use his treatment? Would he be risking great harm to a human life? Perhaps Joseph could live, in spite of his wounds….

He talked to his friends, Dr. Grancher and Dr. Vulpian. These two men knew of his work. They went with him to examine Joseph.

When they finished, they turned to their friend. "The boy will surely die," they said. "But if you try your treatment he at least stands a chance of living. By all means, try it!"

Treatment began that very day. In the days that followed, Dr. Pasteur and Joseph became good friends. The scientist watched his little friend worriedly. What if the treatment did not help….

At last the day came when Joseph received the last and strongest dose of the nerve tissue. Dr. Pasteur waited. That night the light in his laboratory burned on long after all the other houses on the street grew dark and silent.

Morning came. The sun rose. The city came alive with the sounds of horses and heavy wagons in the street below. Suddenly there was the sound of flying feet on the stairway. Once more the laboratory door burst open and Madame Meister stood there.

"Dr. Pasteur!" she cried. "Come!" She was gone.

Louis Pasteur limped hurriedly after her. At last he reached Joseph's room. He stopped, his hand on the doorknob. What would he find inside? Would his little friend be well, or would he…. He pushed open the door.

There, sitting up in the big bed, was a smiling boy. A pale—but healthy—Joseph! Beside him stood his mother, tears in her eyes and a smile on her lips.

Joseph gave a little bound, setting the old wooden bed to creaking. "Good morning, Doctor!" he said to his friend.

The scientist could not answer at once. He closed his eyes and took a deep breath. Thank God! His little friend was alive and well!

At last, once and for all, Louis Pasteur was able to erase from his mind the cries of the people of Arbois.

ELIZABETH BLACKWELL:
A PIONEERING PHYSICIAN
by Vanessa Wright

What do you want to be when you grow up? When six-year-old Elizabeth Blackwell was asked that question, she stuck out her chin and replied, "I don't know what I'm going to be. But I think that it will be something hard!"

The little girl was right. She grew up to become a doctor. That is hard enough. But Elizabeth Blackwell was not only a doctor. She was also a pioneer. That doesn't mean that she traveled west in a covered wagon. It means that she led the way for others by being the first to do something new and difficult.

As you will see, what she did turned out to be very hard to do—harder, perhaps, than she ever imagined.

Young Elizabeth Blackwell grasped the rail of the rolling ship. Her face was pale. Her legs wobbled as if they were made of jelly.

It was the year 1832, and the eleven-year-old girl had been seasick almost every day since she and her family had left England. But as she breathed in the fresh air, her eyes brightened. The sun brought color back to her cheeks.

"Bessie," called Elizabeth's father, striding across the deck, "are you all right?" Many of the passengers in first class had been seasick, and Samuel Blackwell was worried about his daughter.

"Yes, Papa," Elizabeth replied. "I feel better out here." Then she frowned. "Tell me, how many more days will it take us to reach America?"

"Not many," Mr. Blackwell said. "Don't worry, Bessie. Once we land in America, you'll run around and play as though you were never ill."

"It isn't me I'm worried about," said Elizabeth. "I'm just seasick. But the captain said that the people in steerage have cholera."

"Yes," said her father, "that's true."

"Oh, Papa," said Elizabeth, "it's dark and dirty down there. The people can't come up and stand in the sunlight. I heard the captain say that almost half of them have died. And there's no doctor to help them."

Mr. Blackwell looked in his daughter's eyes and asked, "What do you think should be done?"

"Someone needs to help them!" Elizabeth cried. "Papa, you always say that everyone is equal, whether they're black or white, men or women, rich or poor. So why should the poor people in steerage die while everyone on our deck stays healthy?"

"Bessie," said Mr. Blackwell gently, "on almost every long sea voyage, people come down with cholera."

Elizabeth gazed out over the sea. "Then there must be something causing people to get sick," she said. "If doctors could find out what it is, they could tell people about it, and teach them how to stay healthy. Then people wouldn't get sick in the first place."

The little girl turned to her father. "And I shall do it," she said firmly. "When I grow up, I will be a doctor. I will help anyone in need, and I will teach people how to stay healthy."

Mr. Blackwell nodded. "I believe you can, Bessie. I know you can."

But most people who lived during Elizabeth's time did not agree with Mr. Blackwell. They thought that when girls grew up, it was all right for them to be servants, or to work on farms or in factories. But women weren't allowed to become lawyers, bankers, or doctors, or to hold other jobs that were just for men.

Back then, girls received little education. They were not allowed to go to good schools. Many girls did not go to school at all. "Why waste a good education on a girl?" people said. "After all, no woman can do a job as well as a man."

But Mr. Blackwell disagreed. He taught Elizabeth and his other children that all people should have equal rights. He believed that a woman could do a job as well as a man. He taught his daughters subjects that only boys learned in school, such as history and math. And he encouraged his daughters to be whatever they wanted to be.

Elizabeth wanted to be a doctor. She read all the books she could find. She studied with doctors to learn about the human body. She talked with scientists to learn how medicines are made and how they work.

Finally, Elizabeth decided to apply to medical school. Most people said, "A woman doctor—that's ridiculous!" Women were not supposed to go to college in Elizabeth's time. They certainly were not supposed to be doctors.

But Elizabeth was determined. She applied to 29 medical schools. Twenty-eight of the schools said no.

Then, on a crisp October day, she received a letter. Her fingers trembled as she opened the flap. As she read the message, her face lit up. Geneva Medical College, a small school in New York, had accepted her! "I will be a doctor," she cried, and ran inside to pack her bags.

But Elizabeth's struggle had just begun. Many of the students, teachers, and townspeople were shocked and angry when she arrived. Some students called her names. One teacher refused to let Elizabeth into his classroom. The townspeople stared at her and muttered rude things about her. Some children even chased her through the streets, screeching, "Doctor in petticoats! Doctor in petticoats!"

Elizabeth was frustrated, but she did not give up. As she walked to and from her classes, she recited the names of bones and muscles. She studied her books until her tallest candle melted into a puddle of wax. She quickly became the best student in her class. And through it all, she stayed calm and spoke kindly to everyone. Slowly, her courage and determination won the people's respect and friendship.

At last, the day came for Elizabeth to graduate. In the morning, she and her brother, Henry, slipped into the church where the ceremony would be held. When they arrived, many of the seats were already filled with curious women, whispering excitedly to each other. The two took their seats by the aisle.

As the graduates entered the church, the organist began to play. Elizabeth stood and walked to the front row of seats with her fellow classmates.

In groups of four, all the men were called up to receive their diplomas. Elizabeth was called up last of all, and alone. The president of the college took off his hat and presented her with her diploma.

Elizabeth bowed and turned to go back to her seat. Then, suddenly, she said to the president, "Sir, I thank you. By the help of the Most High, it shall be the effort of my life to shed honor upon your diploma."

Elizabeth bowed to the president of the college, and he bowed to her. The audience burst into applause. Then Dr. Elizabeth Blackwell took her seat with her fellow doctors at the front of the church. She had just become the first woman to graduate from a medical college—the first woman doctor.

After she graduated, Dr. Blackwell worked for a while in hospitals in France and England. In 1851, she returned to the

United States. No hospital would hire her. So she bought a house, and there she took care of sick women and children.

She also wrote books that showed people how to stay healthy. She encouraged them to eat right and keep things clean. She also told people not to wait until they were very sick to go to a doctor. She called her teachings preventative medicine. She wanted to prevent disease, to stop it before it started. "Even better than curing ills is seeing that ills do not happen in the first place," she said.

Elizabeth had not forgotten the poor people on the ship that carried her to America so many years before. "Poor women and children need good hospitals, too," she thought. "I will build a place where they can come to get well."

She rented a room in one of the poorest neighborhoods in New York City. Trash was piled up in the front yard. The front door hung on one hinge and banged in the wind. Inside, the room was dirty and bare.

"Isn't there a nicer, cleaner place where we might start a hospital?" asked the women who were helping Elizabeth.

"No," Elizabeth replied. "Good health can start anywhere. And it is most needed right here."

She and her friends cleared the trash out of the yard. They fixed the door. They cleaned and painted the little room, and tacked up pretty curtains. Caring families donated chairs, a desk, a table, and a cot.

Elizabeth put her heavy medical books on one shelf. She placed medicines and bandages on another. She polished her medical instruments and tucked them away in a drawer. Then she threw open the door of the clinic.

For many days, no one came. Then one morning, Elizabeth saw an old woman walking slowly toward the door. She held one arm tightly against her side. Her face was twisted with pain.

The old woman opened the door. She peered into the cheerful room. She saw only Elizabeth sitting at her desk. "Is there no doctor here?" she asked.

Elizabeth replied, "I am the doctor. Come in. I can help you."

Elizabeth helped the old woman get better. After a few days, the old woman returned, leading her sick grandchild by the hand. Behind her huddled a dozen more sick people.

Soon Elizabeth had a line of patients stretching down the block. Many of them had never visited a doctor in their lives. Elizabeth helped them get well. Then she visited their homes to teach them about healthy living. She also got help from a welcome friend—her sister, Emily Blackwell. Emily had just graduated from medical school. She, too, had become a doctor.

The sisters' little clinic grew to become the New York Infirmary for Indigent Women and Children. Here, Elizabeth also started the Women's Medical College to train more women to become doctors.

Following in the footsteps of Elizabeth Blackwell, thousands of women have become doctors. The determined little girl did indeed grow up to do "something hard." Looking back on her life, Dr. Blackwell said, "It is not easy to be a pioneer, but oh, it is fascinating! I would not trade one moment, even the worst moment, for all the riches in the world."

SIR ALEXANDER FLEMING: THE ACCIDENT THAT CHANGED THE WORLD
by Dorothy Haas

Today, you would be shocked to hear that someone died because of a cut. But less than a century ago, this could happen if a cut became badly infected. Now, however, we have drugs called antibiotics to fight infection caused by bacteria. The discovery of the antibiotic called penicillin started with an accident—an accident that changed the world.

In a quiet little laboratory in St. Mary's Hospital on London's Praed Street, a scientist bent over his microscope. He was studying something in a little glass plate called a Petri dish. He looked intently into his microscope for a long moment.

At last he wrote something in his notebook. Then he put aside the Petri dish. He reached for the glass cover to place over it. But before he could cover it, something happened to the dish.

A tiny speck, too small to see, floated in the air above the laboratory bench. The movements of the scientist's arm sent up faint air currents. They caught the speck and wafted it down into the Petri dish. It settled there just before the cover glass was slipped into place. It was a tiny spore, from which mold grows.

Since the mold spore was nearly invisible, the scientist did not see it settle in the dish. If he had, he might have thrown away the contents of the dish at once. For the dish had a special kind of bacteria being grown on a special, pure bacteria food. It was called a "culture." Anything falling into the culture ruined it for laboratory work.

But the scientist didn't see the mold spore fall into his dish. And so the culture was kept.

The scientist was Dr. Alexander Fleming. He was a bacteriologist. His business was the study of those tiny organisms that are the terror of mankind—bacteria that cause sickness and disease.

At the moment Dr. Fleming was working on a paper about a certain kind of bacteria. In order to see them, he had grown the bacteria in his laboratory. He studied them carefully as he worked on his paper. The year was 1929.

Several days passed after the mold spore dropped onto the culture. Once again Dr. Fleming reached for the Petri dish. He took off the cover and placed the dish under his microscope. Then he looked into the instrument's eyepiece. He straightened in surprise.

"Why, what's that?" he said aloud.

He glanced at the window. Praed Street was hidden by a thick London fog.

"Frightfully damp weather!" he exclaimed. "Good for mold, though. Well, as long as it's there, let's have a closer look at it!"

He leaned over his microscope once more, frowning thoughtfully.

The single mold spore had sent out many tiny arms. These had, in turn, sent out arms of their own. The spot of mold had grown bigger and bigger. What Dr. Fleming saw in his microscope was a regular little colony of soft, furry mold growing on top of the bacteria culture.

Suddenly he blinked.

What was that? He adjusted the eyepiece of his microscope and looked more closely. The tiny spot of mold had a ring around it. The ring was free of bacteria. Now here was something interesting!

Dr. Fleming took a test tube. He filled it with a kind of broth, the kind mold likes to grow on. Then, using a platinum wire loop, he picked up some of the mold on the culture. He was very careful not to take any of the bacteria with it. He set the mold down on the broth in the test tube. Then he sealed it with cotton and held it up to the light.

"There, now, little fellow," he said. "Let's see what you'll do in a culture that's all your own!"

He set the mold culture aside to grow. Then he went back to his work on the bacteria culture. His paper had to be done on time.

Several more days went by. The paper was finished and sent off. At last the scientist was free to look at his guests, the mold that had dropped in without invitation and had been asked to stay. He found that the test tube now had a fine growth of fuzzy mold on top of the broth.

Dr. Fleming dipped up some of the mold. He streaked it across a glass plate. Then he put a certain bacteria on the plate. He set it aside and waited to see what would happen.

After a few days he looked at the plate. Some kinds of the bacteria had grown right up to the mold. But other kinds could grow nowhere near it; they had been stopped by it. And they happened to be kinds of bacteria that had always meant serious illness, even death, to man!

Now here was something a bacteriologist could get excited about!

Dr. Fleming knew that certain kinds of bacteria have pitched battles. Each side sends out strong chemicals to try to poison the other side. The stronger bacteria win the war by killing the weaker bacteria.

But nobody had ever suspected that mold could declare war on bacteria—and what's more, win that war!

Dr. Fleming set a great many test tubes of mold culture to growing. Then he dipped up some of the mold and smeared it on a glass slide. He took it to another scientist who knew all about plant life.

"Can you tell me what this queer-looking mold is?" he asked. "It dropped into one of my cultures."

The other man put the slide under his microscope.

"Oh, it's a common enough mold," he said after a time. "Likes to grow where it's cool and damp. Our London housewives are doubtless having their troubles with it this summer too. In weather like this it spoils enough bread and cheese to feed the king's guard for a week!"

He gave the slide back to Dr. Fleming. "It's one of the penicillium family," he said. "I'm not exactly sure which branch of the family it belongs to, though."

Dr. Fleming went back to his laboratory with the slide. Common mold, eh? Well, for a common mold, this little colony of mold spores was performing some very uncommon tricks!

Months passed. Dr. Fleming soon had racks of test tubes, each with a velvety pad of mold on top. He performed many experiments.

As he worked with the mold, he became acquainted with its habits. He found that it did something unusual; it turned the broth on which it grew a brilliant, golden yellow. This gave him a new idea. Maybe the fluid produced by the mold could also kill bacteria.

He began a new series of tests. He streaked his plates with the yellow fluid. He put bacteria on the plates. And he had his answer: the yellow fluid did kill the bacteria.

All of Dr. Fleming's tests had been made on the bacteria themselves. Now he tested the fluid on living cells. The cells did not seem to be harmed by the golden fluid. Was it possible that a fluid so powerful that it stopped bacteria growth would prove harmless to living beings? Dr. Fleming made a series of tests.

He took his golden fluid and went to the room where laboratory animals were kept. He injected it into well animals and sick ones. Then he waited.

Days passed. Each day he visited his little animals. The healthy ones showed no signs of becoming ill. And sick animals, which ordinarily would have died, improved quickly and soon were well. It almost seemed a miracle!

The last day of the animal tests found Dr. Fleming standing before the cages. He was watching the rabbits nibble at their lettuce. The young medical student in charge of the animals stood next to the scientist.

"The stuff you gave them certainly seems to agree with the little chaps!" he said. "Why, that little fellow over there was dying last week! What did you give him, sir?"

Dr. Fleming found a crisp piece of lettuce. He held it inside the cage for the rabbit to nibble.

"It's a filtered fluid produced by a mold of the penicillium family," he explained. "Since I can't very well call it 'mold fluid'"—he smiled—"I call it 'penicillin.'"

The young man tried the word. "Penicillin—penicillin. A queer word, but I imagine one could get used to it."

Then another idea came to him. "I say, Doctor!" he said. "How did you happen to find out the pen—penicillin could cure sickness?"

Dr. Fleming was quiet for a minute, remembering. "It started as something of an accident," he said finally. "After that it was a question of patience and work—good, satisfying work!"

The young man remained next to the rabbit cages after the scientist left the room. He looked down at the rabbit and shook his head.

"Well," he exclaimed, "all I have to say is: It's a lucky day for the human race when 'accidents' happen to men like Dr. Fleming!"

POETRY

A PATCHWORK OF PEOPLE

SOME PEOPLE
by Rachel Field

Isn't it strange some people make
  You feel so tired inside,
Your thoughts begin to shrivel up
  Like leaves all brown and dried!
But when you're with some other ones,
  It's stranger still to find
Your thoughts as thick as fireflies
  All shiny in your mind!

THOUGHTS ON TALKERS
by Walter R. Brooks

Some people talk in a telephone
And some people talk in a hall;
Some people talk in a whisper,
And some people talk in a drawl;
And some people talk-and-talk-and-talk-and-talk-and-talk
And never say anything at all.

TEN KINDS

by Mary Mapes Dodge

Winnie Whiney, all things grieve her;
Fannie Fibber, who'd believe her?
Lotty Loozem, late to school, sir;
Albert Allplay, quite a fool, sir;
Kitty Kissem, loved by many;
George Grump, not loved by any;
Ralph Ruff—beware his fist, sir;
Tillie Tattle, like a blister;
Gus Goodactin, bright and cheery;
Sammy Selfish, sour and dreary.
Do you know them, as I've sung them?
Easy 'tis to choose among them.

GOING TOO FAR

by Mildred Howells

A woman who lived in Holland, of old,
Polished her brass till it shone like gold.
She washed her pig after all his meals
In spite of his energetic squeals.
She scrubbed her doorstep into the ground,
And the children's faces, pink and round,
She washed so hard that in several cases
She polished their features off their faces—
Which gave them an odd appearance, though
She thought they were really neater so!
Then her passion for cleaning quickly grew,
And she scrubbed and polished the village through,
Until, to the rage of all the people,
She cleaned the weather-vane off the steeple.
As she looked at the sky one summer's night
She thought that the stars shone out less bright;
And she said with a sigh, "If I were there,
I'd rub them up till the world should stare."
That night a storm began to brew,
And the wind from the ocean blew and blew
Till, when she came to her door next day
It whisked her up, and blew her away—
Up and up in the air so high
That she vanished, at last, in the stormy sky.

Since then it's said that each twinkling star
And the big white moon, shine brighter far.
But the neighbors shake their heads in fear
She may rub so hard they will disappear!

EAT-IT-ALL ELAINE

by Kaye Starbird

I went away last August
To summer camp in Maine,
And there I met a camper
Called Eat-it-all Elaine.
Although Elaine was quiet,
She liked to cause a stir
By acting out the nickname
Her camp-mates gave to her.

The day of our arrival
At Cabin Number Three
When girls kept coming over
To greet Elaine and me,
She took a piece of Kleenex
And calmly chewed it up,
Then strolled outside the cabin
And ate a buttercup.

Elaine, from that day forward,
Was always in command.
On hikes, she'd eat some birch-bark
On swims, she'd eat some sand.
At meals, she'd swallow prune-pits
And never have a pain,
While everyone around her
Would giggle, "Oh, Elaine!"

One morning, berry picking,
A bug was in her pail,
And though we thought for certain
Her appetite would fail,
Elaine said, "Hmm, a stinkbug."
And while we murmured, "Ooh,"
She ate her pail of berries
And ate the stinkbug, too.

The night of Final Banquet
When counselors were handing
Awards to different children
Whom they believed outstanding,
To every thinking person
At summer camp in Maine
The Most Outstanding Camper
Was Eat-it-all Elaine.

Jimmy Jet and His TV Set

by Shel Silverstein

I'll tell you the story of Jimmy Jet—
And you know what I tell you is true.
He loved to watch his TV set
Almost as much as you.

He watched all day, he watched all night
Till he grew pale and lean,
From "The Early Show" to "The Late Late Show"
And all the shows between.

He watched till his eyes were frozen wide,
And his bottom grew into his chair.
And his chin turned into a tuning dial,
And antennae grew out of his hair.

And his brains turned into TV tubes,
And his face to a TV screen.
And two knobs saying "VERT."and HORIZ."
Grew where his ears had been.

And he grew a plug that looked like a tail
So we plugged in little Jim.
And now instead of him watching TV
We all sit around and watch him.

JONATHAN BING

by Beatrice Curtis Brown

Poor old Jonathan Bing
Went out in his carriage to visit the King,
But everyone pointed and said, "Look at that!
Jonathan Bing has forgotten his hat!"
(He'd forgotten his hat!)

Poor old Jonathan Bing
Went home and put on a new hat for the King,
But by the palace the soldier said, "Hi!
You can't see the King; you've forgotten your tie!"
(He'd forgotten his tie!)

Poor old Jonathan Bing,
He put on a *beautiful* tie for the King,
But when he arrived an Archbishop said, "No!
You can't come to court in pajamas, you know!"

Poor old Jonathan Bing
Went home and addressed a short note to the King:
    If you please will excuse me
    I won't come to tea;
    For home's the best place for
    All people like me!

THE PIRATE DON DURK OF DOWDEE
by Mildred Plew Meigs

Ho, for the Pirate Don Durk of Dowdee!
He was as wicked as wicked could be,
But oh, he was perfectly gorgeous to see!
    The Pirate Don Durk of Dowdee.

His conscience, of course, was black as a bat,
But he had a floppety plume on his hat
And when he went walking it jiggled—like that!
    The plume of the Pirate Dowdee.

His coat it was crimson and cut with a slash,
And often as ever he twirled his mustache
Deep down in the ocean the mermaids went splash,
    Because of Don Durk of Dowdee.

Moreover, Dowdee had a purple tattoo,
And stuck in his belt where he buckled it through
Were a dagger, a dirk and a squizzamaroo,
    For fierce was the Pirate Dowdee.

So fearful he was he would shoot at a puff,
And always at sea when the weather grew rough
He drank from a bottle and wrote on his cuff,
    Did Pirate Don Durk of Dowdee.

Oh, he had a cutlass that swung at his thigh
And he had a parrot called Pepperkin Pye,
And a zigzaggy scar at the end of his eye
    Had Pirate Don Durk of Dowdee.

He kept in a cavern, this buccaneer bold,
A curious chest that was covered with mold,
And all of his pockets were jingly with gold!
    O jing! went the gold of Dowdee.

His conscience, of course, it was crook'd like a squash,
But both of his boots made a slickery slosh,
And he went through the world with a wonderful swash,
    Did Pirate Don Durk of Dowdee.

It's true he was wicked as wicked could be,
His sins they outnumbered a hundred and three,
But oh, he was perfectly gorgeous to see,
    The Pirate Don Durk of Dowdee.

RHINOS PURPLE, HIPPOS GREEN

by Michael Patrick Hearn

My sister says
I shouldn't color
Rhinos purple,
Hippos green.
She says
I shouldn't be so stupid;
Those are things
She's never seen.
But I don't care
What my sister says,
I don't care
What my sister's seen.
I will color
What I want to—
Rhinos purple,
Hippos green.

SINCE HANNA MOVED AWAY

by Judith Viorst

The tires on my bike are flat.
The sky is grouchy gray.
At least it sure feels like that
Since Hanna moved away.

Chocolate ice cream tastes like prunes.
December's come to stay.
They've taken back the Mays and Junes
Since Hanna moved away.

Flowers smell like halibut.
Velvet feels like hay.
Every handsome dog's a mutt
Since Hanna moved away.

Nothing's fun to laugh about.
Nothing's fun to play.
They call me, but I won't come out
Since Hanna moved away.

PETE AT THE ZOO

by Gwendolyn Brooks

I wonder if the elephant
Is lonely in his stall
When all the boys and girls are gone
And there's no shout at all,
And there's no one to stamp before,
No one to note his might.
Does he hunch up, as I do,
Against the dark of night?

POETRY

STORIES IN VERSE

DADDY FELL INTO THE POND

by Alfred Noyes

Everyone grumbled. The sky was grey.
We had nothing to do and nothing to say.
We were nearing the end of a dismal day.
And there seemed to be nothing beyond,
　　THEN
　　Daddy fell into the pond!

And everyone's face grew merry and bright,
And Timothy danced for sheer delight.
"Give me the camera, quick, oh quick!
He's crawling out of the duckweed!" *Click!*

Then the gardener suddenly slapped his knee,
And doubled up, shaking silently,
And the ducks all quacked as if they were daft
And it sounded as if the old drake laughed.
O, there wasn't a thing that didn't respond
　　WHEN
　　Daddy fell into the pond!

MILLIONS OF STRAWBERRIES
by Genevieve Taggard

Marcia and I went over the curve,
Eating our way down
Jewels of strawberries we didn't deserve,
Eating our way down.
Till our hands were sticky, and our lips painted,
And over us the hot day fainted,
And we saw snakes,
And got scratched,
And a lust overcame us for the red unmatched
Small buds of berries,
Till we lay down—
Eating our way down—
And rolled in the berries like two little dogs,
Rolled
In the late gold.
And gnats hummed,
And it was cold,
And home we went, home without a berry,
Painted red and brown,
Eating our way down.

THE ELF AND THE DORMOUSE

by Oliver Herford

Under a toadstool
    Crept a wee Elf,
Out of the rain
    To shelter himself.

Under the toadstool,
    Sound asleep,
Sat a big Dormouse
    All in a heap.

Trembled the wee Elf,
    Frightened, and yet
Fearing to fly away
    Lest he get wet.

To the next shelter—
    Maybe a mile!
Sudden the wee Elf
    Smiled a wee smile,

Tugged till the toadstool
    Toppled in two.
Holding it over him
    Gaily he flew.

Soon he was safe home
    Dry as could be.
Soon woke the Dormouse—
    "Good gracious me!

Where is my toadstool?"
    Loud he lamented.
—And that's how umbrellas
    First were invented.

THE LEAK IN THE DIKE
by Phoebe Cary

The good dame looked from her cottage
   At the close of the pleasant day,
And cheerily called to her little son
   Outside the door at play:
"Come, Peter, come! I want you to go,
   While there is yet light to see,
To the hut of the blind old man who lives
   Across the dike, for me;
And take these cakes I made for him—
   They are hot and smoking yet;
You have time enough to go and come
   Before the sun is set."

Then the good-wife turned to her labor,
   Humming a simple song,
And thought of her husband, working hard
   At the sluices all day long;
And set the turf a-blazing,
   And brought the coarse, black bread;
That he might find a fire at night,
   And see the table spread.

And Peter left the brother,
   With whom all day he had played,
And the sister who had watched their sports
   In the willow's tender shade;
And told them they'd see him back before

They saw a star in sight—
Though he wouldn't be afraid to go
    In the very darkest night!
For he was a brave, bright fellow,
    With eye and conscience clear;
He could do whatever a boy might do,
    And he had not learned to fear.
Why, he wouldn't have robbed a bird's nest,
    Nor brought a stork to harm,
Though never a law in Holland
    Had stood to stay his arm!

And now, with his face all glowing,
    And eyes as bright as the day
With the thoughts of his pleasant errand,
    He trudged along the way;
And soon his joyous prattle
    Made glad a lonesome place—
Alas! if only the blind old man
    Could have seen that happy face!
Yet he somehow caught the brightness
    Which his voice and presence lent;
And he felt the sunshine come and go
    As Peter came and went.

And now, as the day was sinking,
    And the winds began to rise,
The mother looked from her door again,
    Shading her anxious eyes,
And saw the shadows deepen,

And birds to their homes come back,
But never a sign of Peter
    Along the level track.
But she said: "He will come at morning,
    So I need not fret or grieve—
Though it isn't like my boy at all
    To stay without my leave."

But where was the child delaying?
    On the homeward way was he,
And across the dike while the sun was up
    An hour above the sea.
He was stopping now to gather flowers;
    Now listening to the sound,
As the angry waters dashed themselves
    Against their narrow bound.
"Ah! well for us," said Peter,
    "That the gates are good and strong,
And my father tends them carefully,
    Or they would not hold you long!
You're a wicked sea," said Peter;
    "I know why you fret and chafe;
You would like to spoil our lands and homes;
    But our sluices keep you safe!"

But hark! through the noise of waters
    Comes a low, clear, trickling sound;
And the child's face pales with terror,
    And his blossoms drop to the ground.
He is up the bank in a moment,
    And, stealing through the sand,
He sees a stream not yet so large
    As his slender, childish hand.

'Tis a leak in the dike! He is but a boy,
    Unused to fearful scenes;
But, young as he is, he has learned to know
    The dreadful thing that means.
A leak in the dike! The stoutest heart
    Grows faint that cry to hear,
And the bravest man in all the land
    Turns white with mortal fear.
For he knows the smallest leak may grow
    To a flood in a single night;
And he knows the strength of the cruel sea
    When loosed in its angry might.

And the boy! He has seen the danger,
    And, shouting a wild alarm,
He forces back the weight of the sea
    With the strength of his single arm!
He listens for the joyful sound
    Of a footstep passing nigh;
And lays his ear to the ground, to catch
    The answer to his cry.
And he hears the rough winds blowing,
    And the waters rise and fall,

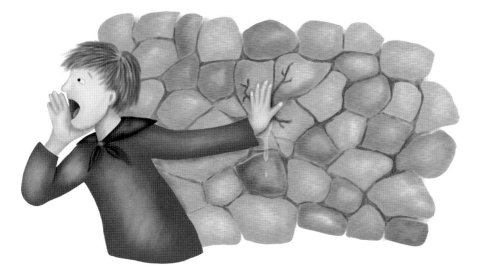

But never an answer comes to him,
    Save the echo of his call.
He sees no hope, no succor,
    His feeble voice is lost;
Yet what shall he do but watch and wait,
    Though he perish at his post!

So, faintly calling and crying
    Till the sun is under the sea;
Crying and moaning till the stars
    Come out for company;
He thinks of his brother and sister,
    Asleep in their safe, warm bed;
He thinks of his father and mother;
    Of himself as dying, and dead;
And of how, when the night is over,
    They must come and find him at last!
But he never thinks he can leave the place
    Where duty holds him fast.

The good dame in the cottage
    Is up and astir with the light,
For the thought of her little Peter
    Has been with her all the night.
And now she watches the pathway,
    As yester-eve she had done;
But what does she see so strange and black
    Against the rising sun?
Her neighbors are bearing between them
    Something straight to her door;
Her child is coming home, but not
    As he ever came before!

"He is dead!" she cries; "my darling!"
    And the startled father hears,
And comes and looks the way she looks,
    And fears the thing she fears:
Till a glad shout from the bearers
    Thrills the stricken man and wife—
"Give thanks, for your son has saved our land,
    And God has saved his life!"
So, there in the morning sunshine
    They knelt about the boy;
And every head was bared and bent
    In tearful, reverent joy.

'Tis many a year since then; but still,
    When the sea roars like a flood,
Their boys are taught what a boy can do
    Who is brave and true and good.
For every man in that country
    Takes his son by the hand,
And tells him of little Peter,
    Whose courage saved the land.

They have many a valiant hero,
    Remembered through the years:
But never one whose name so oft
    Is named with loving tears.
And his deed shall be sung by the cradle,
    And told to the child on the knee,
So long as the dikes of Holland
    Divide the land from the sea!

Adventures of Isabel

by Ogden Nash

Isabel met an enormous bear,
Isabel, Isabel, didn't care;
The bear was hungry, the bear was ravenous,
The bear's big mouth was cruel and cavernous.
The bear said, Isabel, glad to meet you,
How do, Isabel, now I'll eat you!
Isabel, Isabel, didn't worry,
Isabel didn't scream or scurry.
She washed her hands and she straightened her hair up,
Then Isabel quietly ate the bear up.

Once in a night as black as pitch
Isabel met a wicked old witch.
The witch's face was cross and wrinkled,
The witch's gums with teeth were sprinkled.
Ho, ho, Isabel! the old witch crowed,
I'll turn you into an ugly toad!
Isabel, Isabel, didn't worry,
Isabel didn't scream or scurry,
She showed no rage and she showed no rancor,
But she turned the witch into milk and drank her.

Isabel met a hideous giant,
Isabel continued self-reliant.
The giant was hairy, the giant was horrid,
He had one eye in the middle of his forehead.

Good morning, Isabel, the giant said,
I'll grind your bones to make my bread.
Isabel, Isabel, didn't worry,
Isabel didn't scream or scurry.
She nibbled the Zwieback that she
  always fed off,
And when it was gone, she cut the
  giant's head off.

Isabel met a troublesome doctor,
He punched and he poked till
  he really shocked her.
The doctor's talk was of coughs and chills
And the doctor's satchel bulged with pills.
The doctor said unto Isabel,
Swallow this, it will make you well.
Isabel, Isabel, didn't worry,
Isabel didn't scream or scurry.
She took those pills from the pill concocter,
And Isabel calmly cured the doctor.

Mummy Slept Late and Daddy Fixed Breakfast

by John Ciardi

Daddy fixed breakfast.
He made us each a waffle.
It looked like gravel pudding.
It tasted something awful.

"Ha, ha," he said, "I'll try again.
This time I'll get it right."
But what I got was in between
Bituminous and anthracite.

"A little too well done? Oh well,
I'll have to start all over."
That time what landed on my plate
Looked like a manhole cover.

I tried to cut it with a fork:
The fork gave off a spark.
I tried a knife and twisted it
Into a question mark.

I tried it with a hack-saw.
I tried it with a torch.
It didn't even make a dent.
It didn't even scorch.

The next time Dad gets breakfast
When Mummy's sleeping late,
I think I'll skip the waffles.
I'd sooner eat the plate!

HIAWATHA'S CHILDHOOD

by Henry Wadsworth Longfellow

By the shores of Gitche Gumee,
By the shining Big-Sea-Water,
Stood the wigwam of Nokomis,
Daughter of the Moon, Nokomis.
Dark behind it rose the forest,
Rose the black and gloomy pine trees,
Rose the firs with cones upon them;
Bright before it beat the water,
Beat the clear and sunny water,
Beat the shining Big-Sea-Water.

There the wrinkled old Nokomis
Nursed the little Hiawatha,
Rocked him in his linden cradle,
Bedded soft in moss and rushes,
Safely bound with reindeer sinews;
Stilled his fretful wail by saying,
"Hush! the Naked Bear will hear thee!"
Lulled him into slumber, singing,
"Ewa-yea! my little owlet!
Who is this that lights the wigwam?
With his great eyes lights the wigwam?
Ewa-yea! my little owlet!"

Many things Nokomis taught him
Of the stars that shine in heaven;
Showed him Ishkoodah, the comet,
Ishkoodah, with fiery tresses;
Showed the Death-Dance of the spirits,
Warriors with their plumes and war-clubs
Flaring far away to Northward
In the frosty nights of Winter;
Showed the broad white road in heaven,
Pathway of the ghosts, the shadows,
Running straight across the heavens,
Crowded with the ghosts, the shadows.

At the door on Summer evenings
Sat the little Hiawatha;
Heard the whispering of the pine trees,
Heard the lapping of the waters.
Sounds of music, words of wonder;
"Minne-wawa!" said the pine trees,
"Mudway-aushka!" said the water.

Saw the firefly Wah-wah-taysee,
Flitting through the dusk of evening,
With the twinkle of its candle
Lighting up the brakes and bushes,
And he sang the song of children,
Sang the song Nokomis taught him:

"Wah-wah-taysee, little firefly,
Little, flitting, white-fire insect,
Little, dancing, white-fire creature,
Light me with your little candle,
Ere upon my bed I lay me,
Ere in sleep I close my eyelids!"

Saw the moon rise from the water
Rippling, rounding from the water,
Saw the flecks and shadows on it,
Whispered, "What is that, Nokomis?"
And the good Nokomis answered:
"Once a warrior, very angry,
Seized his grandmother, and threw her
Up into the sky at midnight;
Right against the moon he threw her;
'Tis her body that you see there."

Saw the rainbow in the heaven,
In the eastern sky, the rainbow,
Whispered, "What is that, Nokomis?"
And the good Nokomis answered:
"'Tis the heaven of flowers you see there;
All the wild flowers of the forest,
All the lilies of the prairie,
When on earth they fade and perish
Blossom in that heaven above us."

When he heard the owls at midnight,
Hooting, laughing in the forest,
"What is that?" he cried in terror.
"What is that," he said, "Nokomis?"
And the good Nokomis answered:
"That is but the owl and owlet,
Talking in their native language,
Talking, scolding at each other."

Then the little Hiawatha
Learned of every bird its language,
Learned their names and all their secrets,
How they built their nests in Summer,
Where they hid themselves in Winter,
Talked with them whene'er he met them,
Called them "Hiawatha's Chickens."

Of all beasts he learned the language,
Learned their names and all their secrets,
How the beavers built their lodges,
Where the squirrels hid their acorns,
How the reindeer ran so swiftly,
Why the rabbit was so timid,
Talked with them whene'er he met them,
Called them "Hiawatha's Brothers."

TEXT CREDITS AND SOURCES

Stories

"The Bear Boy" from *Flying with the Eagle, Racing the Great Bear* by Joseph Bruchac, copyright © 1993. Reprinted with permission of the author.

"Brer Rabbit Goes Back to Mr. Man's Garden" from *The Tales of Uncle Remus* by Julius Lester, copyright © 1987 by Julius Lester. Used by permission of Dial Books for Young Readers, an imprint of Penguin Putnam Books for Young Readers, a division of Penguin Putnam, Inc.

"Brer Rabbit Gets Brer Fox's Dinner" from *More Tales of Uncle Remus* by Julius Lester, copyright © 1988 by Julius Lester. Used by permission of Dial Books for Young Readers, an imprint of Penguin Putnam Books for Young Readers, a division of Penguin Putnam, Inc.

"From Tiger to Anansi" from *Anansi the Spider Man* by Philip Sherlock, copyright © 1954, reprinted by permission of Macmillan Caribbean.

"The Green Glass Ball" is reprinted with permission of *Plays* Magazine, copyright 1991, Kalmbach Publishing Co., 21027 Crossroads Circle, Waukesha, WI 53187-1612. Web: www.playsmag.com

"How Bear Lost His Tail" from *Iroquois Stories* by Joseph Bruchac, copyright © 1985. Reprinted with permission of the author.

"It Could Always be Worse" from *A Treasury of Jewish Folklore* edited by Nathan Ausubel, copyright © 1948, 1976, Crown Publishers, Inc. Used by permission of Crown Publishers, a division of Random House, Inc.

"Louis Pasteur: Battle With Death" and "Sir Alexander Fleming: The Accident That Changed the World" from *Men of Science* by Dorothy Haas, copyright © 1959, renewed 1987 by Random House, Inc. Used by permission of Golden Books, an imprint of Random House Children's Books, a division of Random House, Inc.

Poems

"Adventures of Isabel" by Ogden Nash, copyright © 1936 by Ogden Nash, renewed. Reprinted by permission of Curtis Brown, Ltd.

"Daddy Fell into the Pond" by Alfred Noyes, reprinted by permission of The Society of Authors as the Literary Representative of the Estate of Alfred Noyes.

Editor: John Holdren

Art Director: Steve Godwin

Designer: Jayoung Cho

Illustrators:
Jayoung Cho
Deborah Wolfe Ltd. (Jerry Dadds, Nancy Harrison, Jeff LeVan, Phillip Small,
Graham Parslow)

ISBN: 1-931728-37-2

Printed by Worzalla, Stevens Point, WI, USA, July 2015,   Lot 072415